G

Contents

SO-ATF-848

The Great Experiment

Preface

In 1996, Congress passed and President Clinton signed into law a significant reform of a runaway entitlement program. Welfare reform had been 20 years in the making, built on the actions of "early mover" states followed by a decade of using federal waivers to promote state innovation. By the mid-1990s, public discourse had matured; empirical lessons were drawn from the reform experiences of several diverse states – California, Wisconsin, New York, and Massachusetts, to name just a few. Debate over the final Personal Responsibility and Work Opportunity Reconciliation Act in 1995 and 1996 was contentious, but by the time Congress took it up, the debate had already been won in the states. Welfare reform was a fait accompli because it had broad support from states across the country – and the final package preserved states' ability to innovate and lead.

Even though the Welfare Reform Act of 1996 brought change to a controversial entitlement, the contentiousness of the debate pales in comparison to the fervid atmosphere that surrounded the 2010 Patient Protection and Affordable Care Act (PPACA). That should give us pause, given that the PPACA was largely about the normally easier political task of granting new entitlements. Even as this book goes to print, the United States Supreme Court has agreed to hear a case brought by 26 state attorneys general, which aims to undo the law. Proponents may argue that this opposition is the result of the AGs' political ambitions, but polls repeatedly observe deep and broad concern about the law and the encroachment of big government from Washington, D.C. The fact is that the politics of the new law are unsettled and it has yet to garner stakeholder support in a number of states.

In short, the debates about the Welfare Reform Act and the PPACA could not have been more different.

The Great Experiment peels back the heated rhetoric over the PPACA and provides a serious examination of how the relationship between states and the federal government impacts health care policy decisions. All parties involved may agree on the need for change, but how can we as a nation translate that need into effective policy decisions? How can we use federalism to move forward with a policy that achieves political consensus, rather than have one party or the other impose its ideological will from Washington, D.C.? *The Great Experiment* answers these questions head-on, outlining a framework for state and federal action.

The book examines past policy decisions with the goal of articulating the roles that states and the federal government should play in developing meaningful health reform and the principles that should guide future policymaking. As a Massachusetts entity, Pioneer Institute has a unique perspective on this debate. Since the Bay State's own experiment was launched in 2006, Pioneer has watched the Health Care Reform Act take on an exaggerated "persona." For some, it embodies all that is wrong about government intrusion into health care markets; for others, it represents all the virtues of government action.

Pioneer has always focused on applying free market approaches to public policy. At the same time, we understand that the application of free markets in the public sphere requires a higher level of accountability to ensure the public trust is upheld. We are interested in state experiments because it is easier to innovate and target solutions at the state level than from Washington.

There is no question that the Massachusetts health care reform law was a bold experiment. From the start, it was likely to succeed in some areas and fail in others. Due to its experimental nature and because it has some features that could leverage the broader application of market forces, Pioneer has chosen not to take an up-or-down position, preferring rather to provide the highest quality empirical analysis. In 2010, we produced an *Interim Report Card* series, the first comprehensive assessment of the law's impact on access, financing and affordability, administration, and cost-effective quality of care. Chapter 7 of *The Great Experiment* updates those reports with the latest data, and shares our findings in a format more accessible to the lay reader.

The reform has indeed worked well in certain regards, but not as well in others. Those who rush to judgment, whether to celebrate or castigate it, forget that even six years on, we are still implementing pieces of the law and are only now starting to gain access to data outcomes that allow for a true empirical analysis.

The Great Experiment is about much more than a single state experiment, or the immediate questions the presidential primary may raise regarding Mr. Romney's term as governor of Massachusetts. Rather, we have assembled some of the best thinkers to outline the options before state and federal officials. Make no mistake about it: *The Great Experiment* aims to lay out a market-oriented blueprint for the next decade – and seeks to do it with the wisdom and balance that come from observing and analyzing a variety of state and federal policy experiences.

Common sense tells us there are distinct limits to what the country can learn about the federal law's workability from the Massachusetts experience. There are important differences between Massachusetts' reform and the new federal law. One reason for those differences is that the Massachusetts reform was crafted with the Bay State's unique culture and market structure in mind. Specifically, it took into account existing funding streams and the Commonwealth's comparatively low percentage of uninsured citizens. (The percentage of people without health insurance in Massachusetts prior to 2006 was 8 percent; 16 states had more than double that amount; some were three times higher.) Chapters 5 and 6 underscore Massachusetts' business culture, which puts a premium on near-universal coverage. The Bay State's health care market is characterized by a significant number of high-income patients, geographic compactness, and world class health care institutions. Laws passed in previous decades also put Massachusetts at a different starting point from almost every other state in the nation: the Bay State already had a revenue stream going to institutions to defray the cost of indigent care, which the 2006 law redirected to poor individuals so they could buy their own insurance.

The federal law paid little attention to existing market structures; ignored local cultures and the vastly different levels of insurance or lack thereof across the country; depended on new taxes and fees rather than re-directing existing funding streams; and, perhaps most importantly, overturned core federal-state relationships in a sector that makes up one-sixth of our economy.

So how do we move forward? That is the theme – truly, the "great experiment" – of this book. What are workable solutions that offer the needed flexibility and respect our federalist government structure? What solutions meet key challenges: the runaway cost of care, questions about quality of care, access to medical services for all residents, and the desire of most Americans to provide coverage for those with pre-existing conditions? How can the United States grapple with exploding Medicaid and Medicare costs?

With more than half the states suing the federal government over the PPACA, bipartisan concern about the feasibility of its implementation, uncertain timelines, restrictions on state policy choices, and the as of yet unknown cost of implementation for the states, it is critical for market proponents to define an alternative direction.

Even without full repeal of the PPACA, the new federal law will run up against reality. Its real price tag is unclear at this time. Experience is more instructive than academic exercises from the Congressional Budget Office, and experience strongly suggests the actual cost will easily dwarf any past entitlement expansion. Unlike Massachusetts, which used existing funds to create subsidies for the poor to purchase insurance, in some states the federal overhaul will require subsidizing nearly the entire population. And there is still the open question of how employers will respond to the economic incentives in the PPACA, which offers generous subsidies when employees move from employer-based coverage to an exchange.

Then there is politics. With the majority of states having Republican governors and Republican-led legislatures – not to mention the distinct possibility that Republicans may control both houses of Congress – even if the

PPACA survives, it will likely be drastically transformed in coming years.

So what is the response? Saying no to the PPACA is not enough.

The market-based answer cannot simply be an overhaul of one-sixth of our economy loosely based on the experience of a red state that, though not Massachusetts, comprises *two or even five percent* of the country's population. The federal government's role is not to pick one "winning" policy and mandate that all states follow it; rather, it is to foster and learn from state experimentation. It is to draw directional lessons, as it did with welfare reform, and encourage states to experiment and learn from each other. It should not stifle innovation or turn states into mere implementers of federal policy dictates.

State-level experimentation is needed to test and ultimately drive the national health care reform debate. As with welfare reform during the 1980s and 1990s, robust experimentation will allow federal officials to draw important lessons from state successes and failures. These experiences offer a lesson in how major reforms are best moved forward in this country.

Congress needs to rediscover the value of federalism. The federal government can play a leading role by providing states with access to grants and technical assistance that help them expand coverage, measure and improve quality, or increase transparency. But state officials should be given flexibility and authority to establish state-based health insurance market reforms targeted at local market conditions. The relationship should be collaborative instead of prescriptive or simply a *de facto* shifting of risk and responsibility to the states.

Is the nation ready to undertake real health care reform? Are our federal and state leaders ready for this great experiment? We have to be; it is now or never.

Jim Stergios
Executive Director
Pioneer Institute

Introduction

As the year 2012 begins, health care in America stands at a dangerous crossroads, but first some good news. In the U.S., our healthcare providers, professional caregivers, and hospitals are capable of delivering safe and effective therapies, many of which were unknown 10 or 20 years ago. Our physicians, biomedical scientists, and biopharmaceutical industry each lead the world in their track records for innovation. Polls indicate that most Americans remain content with the insurance and health care that they receive. Yet these positives belie critical problems residing just beneath the surface of the U.S. health care sector. If not addressed, these problems will create a health care crisis over the next decade and beyond. Enormous and unsustainable problems of cost, organizational dysfunction, access, and quality threaten to undermine the whole system.

How could this be? In March 2010, after a prolonged season of contentious political debate, Congress passed and the President signed the Patient Protection and Affordable Care Act (PPACA). The PPACA was praised as historic by its supporters, who asserted that its insurance mandates would reduce the number of uninsured, one of the major intentions of those crafting the legislation and a broadly endorsed national goal. Another equally important ambition was to tackle the costs of government-sponsored health programs, and to address the overall level of health care spending, viewed as unsustainable and out of line with the quality of the final product.

What of these goals? Supporters described the PPACA as a necessary first step towards additional, but largely unarticulated, changes that would be necessary to eventually produce a health system that will be more available, more affordable, and offers better health care value. So, 24 months after its passage, why the talk of crisis and a need for reform?

In commenting on this legislation several months before its passage, I pointed out that a successful effort to fix the health care system would require an accurate diagnosis of the elements that produced the problems.[1] I suggested that those who crafted the PPACA failed almost entirely to make that diagnosis, with the consequence being a failure to produce an effective remedy. Today, the health industry tries to read the tea leaves regarding implementation of the PPACA's insurance mandates scheduled to begin in 2014 and deal with many other components of the complex legislation. Meanwhile, few serious observers believe that the PPACA did anything significant to address the looming crisis in health care costs and expenditures, either in the government programs of Medicaid and Medicare, or in the private sector. This timely volume from the Pioneer Institute is a welcome addition to the policy debate that will surely heat up as the future of the PPACA and American health care become a major topic in the ensuing election season and beyond. Whichever party prevails in the contests for the Presidency and Congress, critical policy decisions will be needed as the PPACA offers little guidance as to the right path forward.

Why should an industry that provides goods and services that are so highly valued, so subject to potential progress, and so richly remunerative as to account for one sixth of the economy be so fraught with apparently insolvable problems? Some have blamed the crisis on insurance, biopharmaceutical, and hospital companies, but these supposed villains cannot, in my view, account for the problems we face. The problems stemming from these industries are, in fact, symptoms rather than root causes. The companies are all responding to the environment that has been created through tax, regulatory, and other policies that set health care in the U.S. on its current unsustainable and unsatisfactory course.

What are these root causes? First, tax policy that advantages health insurance through employment and shields most Americans from the awareness of how much of their compensation goes towards health insurance rather than wages. The result is a status quo that offers greater tax benefits to wealthier citizens, creates financial hazards at the time of job change for those with medical problems, and unfairly disadvantages those without employer-provided insurance. Second, state and federal regulations impede the capacity of market forces to develop better products and organizational solutions capable of producing better value for consumers. Third, the federal programs of Medicaid and Medicare include design features that are at the core of our problems of cost and quality, and which, by their size and reach, adversely affect other components of the system. Unfortunately, the PPACA has done little or nothing to address these root causes, and its implementation will likely accelerate many of these problems unless it is repealed or amended. But mere opposition to the legislation is insufficient: the problems in our healthcare system are real, alternative reforms are needed, and these are not yet being developed with sufficient rigor or analysis.

How might such reform be accomplished? A fundamental divide exists between reformers who envision solutions through top-down legislation and those who believe that successful reform must unleash market forces now suppressed by poor legislation and regulation. Core reforms that avoid top-down approaches will release health reform from the grip of politics and special interest concerns. The limits of a top-down approach and the opportunities for market-based reform are even greater in a world where consumer health information is omnipresent, personalized medicine is on the rise, and choices in approaches to health care are almost unavoidably increasing. Changes to federal legislation will surely be a necessary element of durable reform. Rather than attempting the impossible –producing detailed and comprehensive outcomes through legislative mandate – such legislation should aim to unleash the innovation that characterizes other elements of our economy and could characterize the health care industry. Federal legislation should also allow variation at the state level and facilitate potentially useful collaborations across state lines.

One laboratory experiment for health reform is going on in Massachusetts.

This experiment is instructive on many levels. But one thing is clear: The insurance mandate has not addressed the rising costs of health care in this state. Legislative ideas for controlling costs involve drastic changes in how care is paid for, how all actors in the system are organized, and how the enormous pot of health care dollars will be distributed differently. It is questionable that the process derived from such a regulatory brew would control costs while stimulating innovation and protecting the interests of the consumers of medical services.

This book helps to frame the vital discussion of the future of health care reform. A distinguished group of contributors, all operating from the perspective that market-based solutions are essential to effective reform, have addressed many of the key issues. They have done so with attention to the lessons learned from reform in Massachusetts, which is being examined closely around the country, even if the lessons that translate to other states may be limited.

Chapter 1 lays out the vision for competitive federalism on health care reform that challenges the current federal and state relationship. Tom Miller identifies the limits to state-led health policy correction and pinpoints the federal policy barriers obstructing movement forward. The proposed policy solutions don't account for the entire spectrum of deficiencies in the medical, insurance, and financing structures of the health care sector; instead, they target an important subset of reforms better accomplished at the state level. In subsequent chapters, Miller explains how, in a competitive federalism environment, federal policy can assist, instead of obstruct, these reforms.

In **Chapter 2**, Miller scrutinizes the real and imagined problems associated with providing care to those with pre-existing conditions. He reviews the historical policy reasons for our current predicament, and he also assesses the true scope of the high-risk population requiring coverage. Miller pulls apart the PPACA-designed high-risk pools and lays out principles that states and the federal government should consider in order to operate targeted and effective high risk pools to insure the most ailing among us.

Chapter 3 argues for more opportunities for consumer-directed regulation of insurance at the state level. Miller lays out design features for interstate regulatory competition to facilitate greater choice for consumers. He examines the spillover effects of leveraging greater transparency of health care data for consumers. In the process, he also reviews the efforts of several states to collect data in order to draw lessons for how best to utilize this information as a tool to eventually bend the cost curve.

Chapter 4 tackles the dysfunctional relationship between states and the federal government that currently exists in the Medicaid program. It proposes a transition to a defined contribution model for most Medicaid recipients to allow for greater consumer engagement and state-level creativeness. The perverse incentives in the current program are contrasted to block grant proposals. Miller then summarizes upcoming Medicaid challenges under the PPACA. The chapter also examines possible working models for state-based reformation in Rhode Island and Florida.

Chapter 5 broadens the discussion from single program reforms to one state's experiment currently in progress. Veteran journalist Jennifer Powell recounts the political and policy debates that led to the 2006 reform in Massachusetts. She highlights the important disagreements during the legislative debate that continue to influence the law's implementation. The chapter succinctly outlines the early implementation of important provisions of the law.

In **Chapter 6**, Josh Archambault adroitly describes the influence that the different occupants of the Governor's office (and their appointees) have had on the implementation of the 2006 Massachusetts reform law. The chapter details eight key provisions of the law and highlights how many have differed in implementation from the original vision of reform. Archambault describes the policy provisions that were implemented by the Romney administration and later modified by the Patrick administration, and in which stark differences in ideology emerge. The chapter gives a full treatment of key provisions that were implemented solely by the Patrick administration, discussing how some deviated from provisions and ideas discussed during the policy debate. Finally, Archambault makes a convincing case that current outcome data from Massachusetts must be understood through the lens of these implementation decisions, *at least as much* as the original provisions of the law.

Chapter 7, written jointly by Amy Lischko and Josh Archambault, evaluates the latest data from the experiment in Massachusetts. The chapter strongly cautions against extrapolating conclusions from the Massachusetts experiment and applying them directly to the federal law. Lischko and Archambault evaluate data pre to post reform for (1) access to insurance and to health care services, (2) cost to individuals, employers, and the government, and (3) quality measures for acute and chronic care in the Bay State.

Chapter 8 addresses the lessons and limitations of health insurance exchanges, which entered the national lexicon through the PPACA. Despite the lengthy federal legislation and regulations addressing exchanges and the enormous impact that they will likely have on the health care system, much remains unclear. Lischko describes the lessons that can be learned from Utah and Massachusetts, both states with active public exchanges. What hangs in the balance is whether the exchanges will facilitate or hinder the health care system's needed reform.

In the **concluding chapter**, Jim Capretta outlines an agenda for state leaders and the next Congress to move the U.S. towards more market-based reforms of the health care system. He discusses the two possible paths ahead for the country in health policy: either market-driven reforms or government-imposed cost controls. Given his experience at the Office of Management and Budget, Capretta outlines the chilling budgetary future that faces our nation with its escalating health care costs. Capretta rightly argues that the only effective reforms will be ones that (1) allow for a functioning marketplace to compel cost discipline without sacrificing quality, and (2) respect federalism. He lays out specific policy proposals such as state implementation of federally-financed tax credits for coverage, addressing pre-existing conditions with state-based high risk pools, and state implementation of market-based Medicaid reforms.

Reforming the health care sector through the political process is a daunting task. Existing conditions favor some stakeholders and harm others, and tackling these conditions through legislation unleashes a multitude of special interests, leaving the average citizen unprotected. The only antidote is information, carefully researched and well presented. This book will hopefully play an important role in moving the health care discussion forward. Regardless of the political outcomes in 2012, our leaders must find effective solutions that allow for a health care marketplace that provides us the high-quality and lower-cost system that we have always wanted as consumers.

Jeffrey S. Flier
Dean of Harvard Medical School
Boston, Massachusetts

Part 1
Competitive Federalism

1

The Case for Competition, Choice, and a Healthy Federalism

Tom Miller

Both the rhetoric and the reality of health care federalism have become more evident in recent discussions of health policy reform that took place immediately before and well after the enactment of the Patient Protection and Affordable Care Act (PPACA) in March 2010. State governments traditionally have been dominant in regulating fully insured health care plans and the practice of medicine; determining the parameters of their Medicaid programs beyond federally required minimums; and using their "police powers" to monitor and improve the public health of their citizens. However, the federal government has increasingly used its own substantial powers to tax, spend, and regulate in order to control more and more health policy decisions. In many ways, passage and early implementation of the PPACA will continue that trend on an even larger scale. However, the law's numerous equivocations and ambiguities, a robust counter-reaction by many state leaders, and several challenges to the constitutionality of the broader federal power over health care that the PPACA claims, have opened new opportunities for a re-assertion of state-level leadership and innovation in health policy.

Even without the looming burdens and risks of the PPACA ahead, the case for relying on a more vigorously competitive version of health policy federalism is strong. The most promising opportunities involve states' policy options for (1) providing a more sustainable safety net for their citizens who face greater health risks and limited access to affordable insurance coverage; (2) encouraging greater choice and competition in health insurance across state lines; (3) restructuring Medicaid to be more targeted, effective, and patient-centered; and (4) improving the transparency of information about the cost, quality, and value of health care treatment options in local markets. To take full advantage of these opportunities, states will need to be creative and forceful. Also, important federal policy barriers to competition and choice in regional and local markets, including several key provisions of the PPACA, will have to be lowered, if not eliminated.

Starting Points to Address Chronic Problems

The core problems in the U.S. health care system are broader than just the easier-to-measure ones involving levels of insurance coverage and the rising cost of health insurance premiums. Lack of access to more affordable health care options in the United States fundamentally reflects the longstanding trend for the annual rate of growth in health care costs to exceed annual growth in the rest of the economy (approximately 2 -2.5 percent higher than in the rest of the economy per year over the last four decades, depending on the period measured). Although this basic relationship is ultimately unsustainable (we can't all join the health care sector and pay ourselves for providing our own treatment, and we have other needs and preferences for consumption, saving, and investment), the imbalance has become more acute in recent years as the overall economy's growth slowed, government budget deficits ballooned, and enrollment in taxpayer-financed health entitlement programs surged. Longstanding demographic trends (an aging population with longer life expectancy) further aggravate the gap between the sunk costs of political promises to the elderly and the ability of the current and future working population to finance these promises through leveraged intergenerational financing.

This economic resource mismatch is compounded by several other basic problems. Health care quality remains significantly uneven across different areas of the country and to a somewhat lesser extent within local markets. The actual value of particular health care services that are delivered in practice often remains inadequate or unknown due to lack of transparent, relevant, robust, and usable information about these services. The market-based cost of health care services is distorted and obscured by three primary factors: heavy layers of regulation at the federal and state level, mandated benefits, substantial open-ended taxpayer subsidies, and a financial structure in which almost nine-tenths of all health care spending is determined by third-party payers (taxpayers, insurers, employers) rather than first-party patients. Competition in health care markets is hampered by increased consolidation among health care providers (particularly in the hospital sector) and regulatory barriers to entry and exit.

Because public and private forms of health insurance coverage finance a large share of all health spending in the U.S., public policies that shape many of its operating rules – whom it covers, which benefits it offers, what it reimburses, and how much it pays – tend to capture a disproportionate share of attention from policymakers and their constituents (most notably in the past and continuing debate over the PPACA). However, the scope, scale, and cost of health insurance largely reflects (1) what providers of health care services deliver, how effectively and efficiently they perform, and the prices they can charge; and (2) the type, frequency, persistence, and complexity of the demands and needs that patients present to them.

This chapter does not address the full panoply of chronic public policy challenges involving delivery system reform, health care decision-making, population health, and health care financing. Instead, it views an important subset of those issues in the context of what can be better accomplished at the state level through "health policy federalism" and how federal policy can help rather than hinder such initiatives.

What States and Their Citizens Can and Should Do

The basic case for a more vigorous brand of competitive federalism in health policy extends well beyond historical nostalgia for simpler and more idealized times of decentralized governance and constitutional constraints on the reach of the federal government's powers and activities. The argument also needs to involve more than an irresponsible political illusion in which one simply imagines that a different level of government will easily discover and execute solutions that have escaped the capabilities of the largest and most centralized one. Instead, facilitating greater jurisdictional competition among states to provide the public goods of health care and regulate private ones should be designed to limit the scope and scale of each state's current monopoly-like political powers based on geographic factors alone. Simply awarding exclusive, but largely unchecked, control over health policy to each individual state – instead of placing it at the national government level – would merely limit the reach of each health policy franchise to individuals living within its physical boundary lines.

Allowing residents of a state more clearly defined "exit rights" – with an option to choose a different type or level of health insurance regulation offered by another state – could help market-like forces of competition reshape the issues of health care politics still delegated to state-level decision-making. It would essentially push rival political institutions to pre-commit to particular terms and limits in order to attract a larger voluntary market share. A well-designed structure for competitive federalism in state-level health policy regulation could limit the overly broad bundling of more heterogeneous preferences through political mechanisms. Competition at the state level would sort and efficiently match them into smaller and more sustainable categories. By reducing the size and scale of political bargaining, competitive federalism would facilitate mobility and internalize better the varied risk/reward consequences of decisions by buyers, sellers, and regulators.

Different states can experiment with new and varied policy alternatives without blowing up the entire national laboratory. States can test and demonstrate new models of policy reform until their broader adoption reaches a critical tipping point for more of a national policy consensus. Initial state-level policy making does not need to assemble a nationwide, super-majority consensus to drive policy change; reaching decisions in individual states faces much lower political transaction costs than larger efforts at the national level. States can adjust more readily to local variations in health care preferences, resources, and capabilities. They can fine-tune initial policy settings with shorter feedback loops and more rapid political response times.

Limits to State-Led Health Policy Innovation

To be sure, theoretical proposals for health policy federalism should respect its practical limits. The structure of U.S. health care regulation was quite fractured before enactment of the PPACA, and it remains so afterward. The regulation of a particular health insurance product or service is largely determined by the type of entity that pays for it. For example, self-insured employer-sponsored health plans (so-called ERISA plans) are largely exempt from state-level regulation, and their primary federal regulator (the Department of Labor) exercises a relatively light hand for various historical, legal, and administrative reasons.[1] Fully-insured employer group health plans and health insurance plans purchased in the individual market are regulated primarily by the states in which they are purchased, reflecting Congress's decision in the 1945 McCarran-Ferguson Act to delegate such regulation to the states. (The degree to which states will remain primary regulators after the PPACA is fully implemented remains less certain, and will be discussed further below.)

Almost half of all health spending is controlled by administrators of public health programs like Medicare and Medicaid or their intermediaries, and such health insurance operates under very different sets of rules and regulations. Although states have a larger role as Medicaid administrators, they still must comply with a substantial set of minimum coverage and benefit mandates, administrative practices, and beneficiary protections required under federal law. In addition to these fragmented spheres of health insurance regulation, other federal and state regulations vary based on the size of an employer that purchases group insurance for its workers. Those rules reflect the different thresholds and ceilings set for small group coverage rules under the Health Insurance Portability and Accountability Act (HIPAA) and the Consolidated

Omnibus Budget Reconciliation Act (COBRA).[2] Moreover, the net cost of insurance coverage for different types of purchases can vary significantly under federal income tax laws, because subsidies under the tax exclusion for employer-sponsored coverage are much more generous than the limited ones available for individual purchasers.[3]

States also face other longstanding institutional constraints that limit how much health reform they can achieve on their own. The biggest ones are financial. States remain dependent on federal assistance (particularly for Medicaid program expenses) due to political, legal, and economic barriers to broadening their revenue base or borrowing more funds. Even exploiting Federal Matching Assistance Percentage (FMAP) formulas and demonstration program waivers to capture additional Medicaid dollars from the federal government has its limits, particularly for those states that fail to get to the front of the line while capped amounts of appropriated funds for experimental policy purposes remain available, or before new budgetary pressures limit the open-ended generosity of matching dollars from Washington. States also can only roll back Medicaid reimbursement rates for providers to the point at which they encounter serious problems in ensuring sufficient participation by doctors and adequate access to them for program beneficiaries.

States cannot independently change the subsidy rules of the Internal Revenue Code for private health insurance. Nor can they try to impose insurance benefits mandates, funding contributions, and pricing restrictions on self-insured employer plans; or prevent many fully-insured employer plans from switching to self-insured status in order to escape more burdensome state insurance regulation. To the extent that state policymakers ignore the underlying drivers of health care costs or try to manage too many politically complex and personal health decisions and their tradeoffs, they will fail as badly as similar efforts by federal policymakers have. The policy challenges involved in setting adequate and sustainable floors that guarantee access to necessary, yet affordable, health care — without resorting to ceilings on rewards for achievement and innovation — are just as great at the state level as at the federal one. States should not hope to fare any better than the federal government in trying to make up their losses on volume from too-generously subsidized health benefits or too-inadequately compensated health care services, overcharging unwilling contributors, or treating the heterogeneous too homogeneously. Despite these limits on the scope and scale of state policy initiatives in health policy, states retain a number of advantages if they choose to take a more assertive role in (1) ensuring access to necessary health care for individuals with serious pre-existing health conditions, (2) expanding choices in the types of regulation of health insurance their residents face, (3) restructuring Medicaid programs to more efficiently align their promises with sustainable resources, and (4) developing and disseminating actionable information for better health care decisions.

Breaking through the Walls of Federal Policy

However, this vision of effective state innovation in health policy reform must operate in the near term within an uncertain and far-from-hospitable federal policy climate. Many of the final policy parameters and regulatory settings of the recently enacted PPACA remain ambiguous and unresolved, if not inherently contradictory and unable to be administered. Their political shelf life also remains in doubt, pending further action in the courts, Congress, and the November 2012 election season.

The new health law presents a thin veneer of federal-state partnership, in which the most difficult and uncertain tasks — implementation of new health benefits exchanges, administration of vastly expanded Medicaid coverage, operation of pre-existing condition insurance plans, and regulation of fully-insured health plans — are delegated initially to state officials. In each case, however, state officials are kept on a relatively short leash and must operate within a narrow sphere of federal policy guidance. Even the dispensation of short-term waivers from the federal government is limited to a handful of the PPACA's requirements, and not even presidential-level executive orders can override the (occasionally) clear language of most provisions of the final law. A recent Congressional Research Service memorandum to Senator Tom Coburn concluded that a President would not appear to be able to issue an executive order halting statutorily required programs or mandatory appropriations for a new grant or other program in the PPACA when it would conflict with an explicit congressional mandate and be viewed as "incompatible with the express will of Congress."[4] Where the PPACA leaves discretion to the Secretary of HHS to take actions to implement a mandatory program, there may be a stronger legal case for an executive order by a President that directs the Secretary to take particular actions in carrying out that discretion. However, legal scholars continue to disagree over whether this is appropriate under the theory of the "unitary executive" (the presidential power to direct the executive branch) or that it would conflict with the "conventional" administrative law view that Congress has delegated the relevant discretion in administrative policymaking only to a specified agency official, rather than to the President. The President is constitutionally required to "take Care that the Laws be faithfully executed" and cannot act as an independent lawmaker contrary to the express or implied will of Congress.

In addition, a recent legislative proposal by Sen. Wyden (D-OR) and Sen. Brown (R-MA) to move up the date from 2017 to 2014 for certain types of state waivers would only allow states to try to find somewhat different means to achieve at least the exact same results required by the PPACA for affordable, near-universal health insurance coverage.

So the "federalism" street often is a narrow and treacherous one, and it may run in different one-way directions depending on who is really in charge and which policy results are sought. Some states can attempt to make the best of a difficult situation while taking a larger share of political heat for cleaning up and completing the unfinished work of the previous Congress that approved the PPACA. In any case, the window of opportunity for successful state health policy innovation has narrowed substantially. Both old and new barriers to state reform stand in the way. They include:

- Federal tax policy for health insurance that still favors employer-sponsored health plans, distorts health care spending patterns, and discriminates against other types of insurance coverage
- A sweeping scheme of expanded federal insurance regulation that

eventually would impose its new rating restrictions and benefits mandates on *all fully insured* health plans by 2014

- Proposed rules for state-based health benefits exchanges that promise to place state officials in the back seat rather than at the steering wheel for key policy decisions as the exchanges are fully implemented
- An early exit for the new federal government-run version of high-risk pools, along with the elimination of both old and new state-run pools by 2014
- Data aggregation, health care measurement, and health information provisions in the PPACA that ensure a centralized, top-down approach to determining "value-based" health care incentives
- A "Medicaid on steroids" coverage expansion that will further stress overstretched state budgets, severely limit reconfiguration of pre-PPACA Medicaid coverage, and crowd out private insurance alternatives for lower-income working adults
- A Medicare program that was only weakened, remains fundamentally unreformed by the PPACA, still threatens to reach insolvency in less than a decade, and will further destabilize the federal budget and the lives of tens of millions of seniors

In short, there is much real health reform needed at both the state and federal levels. It will take a few more shovels both to bury most, if not all, of the PPACA and then to dig a way out to a market-based solution that relies on state-level policy innovation in key areas. The next three chapters will lay the groundwork for this effort by proposing a solution to protect those with serious pre-existing health conditions, regulatory reforms and transparency efforts to foster greater choice and competition in health insurance and health care services, and finally, a method to reform the Medicaid program to make it more accountable both to taxpayers and to its beneficiaries.

2

Confronting Pre-Existing Condition Problems (Real and Imagined)

Tom Miller

A key political argument advanced for passage of the PPACA was that the only way to solve the serious problem of covering vulnerable Americans with pre-existing conditions is through a massive transformation of America's health care system into a far-reaching federal health insurance entitlement — one that will increase costs, raise taxes, displace millions of the currently insured, and undermine our private insurance sector. However, far better targeted solutions are available through a different type of federal-state partnership that relies on redesigned and robustly funded high-risk pools.[1]

The challenge of covering people with pre-existing conditions stems primarily from the limitations of how our largely employer-based and voluntary private health insurance system has evolved amidst complex subsidies and regulations that favor some insurance purchasers over others. Most working Americans get health insurance as an employment benefit.[2] But this means that when they lose or change jobs, they also risk losing or changing their insurance coverage. Accordingly, most people are not continuously covered by the same plan throughout their lives, and they change plans fairly frequently. (Median job tenure has remained fairly stable in recent decades, and it only averages about three years.)[3] If a worker moves directly from one employer-sponsored health plan to another, the disruption is usually not a problem (for reasons discussed below). But whenever someone, by choice or necessity, leaves employer-sponsored insurance to purchase health insurance independently, the switch in coverage presents several risks and challenges.

Insurers competing in a voluntary individual insurance market need to prevent significant mismatches between the premiums they take in and the claims they will need to pay. If an insurer offers coverage to a consumer who has waited until he or she is sick to purchase and enroll in an individual insurance plan without pricing the expected costs of the enrollee's illness into the premium, the expense of paying out medical claims will likely exceed the premiums collected. Moreover, such one-sided offers will encourage others to wait to buy insurance until they need to draw on it. Why pay for insurance when you're healthy if you can buy it for the same price when you get sick? This extreme version of adverse selection would threaten the solvency of insurers if left unaddressed.

Before enactment of the PPACA or more limited policy measures adopted in a handful of states during the 1990s,[4] insurers selling directly to individual consumers in most states relied on three practices to prevent widespread adverse selection. First, they try to take into account the health status of prospective customers when determining their premiums (the underwriting process). They consider an applicant's age and other demographic factors and, in certain cases, medical history, which may lead them to charge a higher premium. Second, in a much smaller percentage of applications for insurance, they may deny coverage of pre-existing conditions for a set period of time after a customer enrolls, so that if the customer buys insurance (or changes insurers) only after being diagnosed with a costly condition, that customer cannot immediately use the new coverage to pay for medical claims associated with the previously existing ailment. Third, insurers may refuse to offer any coverage at all in cases presenting unusually high risks of very costly medical conditions. Taken together, these practices have led to the pre-existing condition problem: People who become sick and do not already have (or no longer have maintained) health care coverage can find themselves without the ability to secure new coverage at an affordable price, sometimes through no fault of their own.

However, the problem of coverage for pre-existing conditions remains relatively limited despite exaggerated rhetoric used by some politicians to advance larger health policy agendas. Senior citizens can obtain health-care coverage fairly automatically through Medicare at age 65. Many low-income Americans qualify for Medicaid regardless of their health status, and others qualify because they suffer from disabling health conditions. Most Americans (and their dependents) who have and maintain employer-based coverage do not run across the pre-existing condition problem. It primarily affects a subgroup of less-healthy, working-age Americans: This includes those who do not receive health coverage from their employers; those who do not qualify for Medicaid; and those who are not able to buy coverage in the individual market because their health conditions causes insurers to charge them much higher premiums, restrict their coverage, or refuse to cover them. Why are pre-existing conditions much less of an issue in the much larger employer-based insurance market? Job-based plans are implicitly "community rated" products — meaning that everyone who is covered by the same plan is charged more or less the same price. Underwriting of individual workers is minimal even in smaller firms (such explicit underwriting is rarely seen in firms with ten or more employees), because insurers sell group plans to firms based on the risk profile of the entire work force. The potentially high costs of paying for the health care needs for some workers with seriously acute or chronic conditions are balanced by the relatively low costs associated with their generally more numerous healthy co-workers. Risk levels in employer plans are also somewhat contained by the pre-screened nature of employer-sponsored insurance. Only relatively healthy people are likely to show up to work regularly, stay employed, and gain access to job-related insurance benefits.

Of course, no technique for managing the risks of highly concentrated health conditions and predictably higher health care claims costs works perfectly. Some smaller firms may have fewer healthy workers in their pool of health risks to balance an occasional high-cost risk. In some industries or job categories, the balance between new "healthy" workers and older "unhealthy" ones may be unfavorably tipped by demographic and economic factors. Even within larger firms, there is evidence that employers sometimes selectively reduce cash wages (or offer lower salary increases) to adjust for the cost of insuring some workers (particularly older and more obese ones) whose actual health care expenses are likely to be much higher than average. Still, on the whole, the sick and the healthy pay roughly the same premiums in job-based plans. Insurers see this approach to pricing employer-sponsored insurance as a sustainable business practice as long as a large majority of workers in a firm enroll in the group's health plan, because selling to a group not only allows for the balancing of high and low risks, it also lowers administrative and marketing costs.

Moreover, in 1996, Congress provided an additional protection for workers. HIPAA made it unlawful for employer-sponsored plans to impose exclusions on pre-existing conditions for workers with sufficient periods of continuous group insurance coverage. This means that if a person stays covered by job-based plans long enough (roughly eighteen months ensures total protection, but lesser intervals still can provide partial protection against shorter pre-existing exclusion periods) with only very short periods of interruption in this continuous coverage, that person can move from one job to another without fear of losing insurance protection, or of having to wait longer than other new hires before gaining coverage for ailments developed before taking a new job. The new employer's plan must provide coverage on the same terms as it is offered to other employees — even if the worker already has developed an expensive medical condition, or demonstrated early indications that it may develop in the near future.

In theory, HIPAA also provided portability rights to people moving from job-based plans to individually owned coverage. The law gave state governments a few options for meeting this mandate: They could establish high-risk pools (which, as discussed below, is the approach most states have followed); they could require that all individual-market health insurers within their respective states offer insurance to all eligible individuals, without any limits on coverage of pre-existing medical conditions; or they could use their regulatory powers to create a mix of rules that would have similar results.

But unfortunately, none of these approaches has worked well enough. Too many people still risk falling through the cracks. One problem in the pre-PPACA world of federal health law stemmed from HIPAA's requirement that a worker first exhaust the right to temporary continuous coverage under the former employer's plan (through a federal program called COBRA, which lets a worker keep buying into a previous employer's insurance plan, generally for up to 18 months after leaving that job) before entering the individual insurance market without being subject to a pre-existing condition exclusion. Many workers are not aware of this requirement (though their former employers must advise them of it in a written notice). Even if they are, the premiums required to stay in an employer's plan through COBRA are often too high for workers to pay on their own. COBRA premiums must cover both the employer and employee share of costs, and such employer plans generally provide more expensive comprehensive benefits than individual-market alternatives. Unlike premiums paid in employer-based plans, these COBRA premiums do not receive any tax advantage[5] — making them even more expensive to workers between jobs and/ or other employer-sponsored coverage. As a result, many workers experience the "sticker shock" of facing this fully loaded price for the first time. They choose not to pay the noticeably higher premiums and take the risk of going without coverage until they can find new jobs (and new coverage). In so doing, they may inadvertently waive their HIPAA rights — leaving themselves vulnerable to exclusions and high costs for pre-existing conditions when they finally try to buy insurance on their own.

Even if a sick person abides by HIPAA's requirements and remains continuously insured — thereby maintaining protection from pre-existing condition exclusions in the individual market — nothing in current federal law prevents insurers from charging this individual more than they charge healthy people (this may eventually change if certain PPACA provisions are maintained in law and eventually implemented fully in 2014). Insurers are prohibited only from denying coverage altogether for a pre-existing condition; it is quite permissible, however, for insurance providers to charge unaffordable premiums (unless an individual state's laws happen to prevent or restrict the practice), thus producing essentially the same outcome.

Pre-PPACA law and regulations also provided no premium protections for persons moving between individual insurance policies. A healthy worker who leaves an employer plan for the individual market might find an affordable plan at first — but if he ever wanted to switch insurers (or was forced to by moving to a new state, for example), he would face the risk of having his premium recalculated based on a new health-risk assessment.

However, the problem of pre-existing condition coverage is limited almost entirely to the individual market. In 2008, at the request of the U.S. Department of Health and Human Services, health economists Mark Pauly, Bradley Herring, and Xue Song examined how people with chronic health conditions, and thus high anticipated health-care expenses, actually fared when seeking insurance in the individual market. Pauly and his co-authors found little, if any, evidence that enrollees in poor health generally paid higher premiums for individual insurance. Nor did they find that the onset of chronic conditions is necessarily associated with increased premiums in subsequent years.[6] Existing "guaranteed renewability" requirements in federal and state law already prevent insurers from continuously reclassifying people (and the premiums they pay) based on health risks. And most private insurers already provided such protection as standard business practice before they were legally required to do so.[7]

Although the risks of facing coverage exclusions and prohibitive premiums caused by pre-existing conditions are not a universal problem in the individual insurance market, they clearly affect many Americans. Reasonable estimates range from 2 to 4 million, out of a total population of about 260 million people under the age of 65.[8] More important than this number alone, however, is how many more Americans know someone who has faced this situation directly, and fear that they could find themselves in the same predicament. The latter perception explains the strong public support for changing the way insurance companies treat pre-existing conditions. Most people find it unacceptable that other citizens who have tried to act responsibly by staying insured throughout their lives can suddenly find themselves sick, perhaps unemployed as well, and unable to get adequate coverage.

On the other hand, in order to stay financially solvent, insurers clearly need some way to match premiums and likely claims costs. Because the smaller individual market often operates as a last resort for those lacking better insurance options through employers, insurers must plan for the risk that people seeking individual coverage are more likely to do so because they believe they will need substantial medical attention.

Nevertheless, there are both practical limits and basic business incentives that restrain excessive underwriting by insurers. For one thing, individual screening of health risks is expensive. Moreover, if insurers screen too aggressively, they will lose customers whose care would not in fact have been very costly. Insurance companies balance the benefits of screening against these costs in the individual market no less than in others: Indeed, the most extensive research in this area, by Pauly and Herring, has demonstrated that there is already a great deal of pooling of health risks in the individual market.[9] But some people clearly have not been able to get covered due to the higher health risks they present to potential insurers.

Long-Term Protection against Future Changes in Health Risk Status

The most effective solution would not be heavy-handed regulation, but rather a new insurance marketplace built around truly portable, individually owned insurance. If individuals and families, instead of their employers, chose and controlled their own insurance plans, people would no longer face the risks that come with changing coverage based on changes in their employment arrangements. By carrying the same insurance plan from one job to the next (or even through periods with no job at all), individuals could keep their coverage even as their health status changed. They also would need to engage in a more careful process of evaluating and choosing the insurance plan in which they initially enroll, because it would involve much more than a one-year decision. Moreover, insurers would have strong incentives to help keep their enrollees healthy, because some of them could be enrolled for many years. That is how health insurance that reduces current health risks and protects against less foreseeable future risks is supposed to work.

But moving to true insurance portability will require fundamental reform of the tax treatment of health insurance in order to level the playing field between insurance plans owned by employers and those owned by individuals. There will also need to be a reworking of some current insurance regulations, information disclosure practices, and insurers' business models. For now, such far-reaching reforms face long political odds, even if the more complex and counterproductive set of insurance rules to be implemented by 2014 under the PPACA were reconsidered. Moreover, if the most elegant portability reforms suggested above were to be adopted instead to protect many individuals against future changes in their health status, they still would not address how to cover people who already suffer from costly health conditions (and thus could not easily afford to purchase their own risk-based portable insurance, even once a new system got up and running).

Short of such a long-term transformation, the more immediate focus of health policy should be aimed most at people shut out by the current system due to their current health status. Some states have attempted to address the problem by imposing risk-rating restrictions on health-insurance premiums. Those rules include requiring insurers to sell to all comers, regardless of their health status (guaranteed issue) and at standard average rates (community rating). But this approach has proven unsustainable, because it causes private insurers to increase the premiums they charge everyone else — particularly younger and healthier customers — in order to make up for the losses associated with the enrollment of more expensive cases at below-cost premiums.[10] And when premiums rise for the former types of current and potential customers in a voluntary marketplace, a significant number of these people — weighing the low short-term risk of an expensive illness against the immediately higher cost of buying health insurance — will drop out of coverage altogether. As the pool of enrollees thus becomes older and less healthy, this is likely to further drive up premium costs for the enrollees who remain. The resulting vicious cycle triggered by excessive regulation that tries to suppress market signals can cause so many consumers and insurers to stop buying and selling insurance that the entire market (particularly the smaller and more precarious individual market) can threaten to collapse. This happened in Washington state and Kentucky when such reforms were tried in the mid-1990s, before they had to be "repealed and replaced."[11]

A more comprehensive, but similarly flawed, approach to health insurance under the PPACA now aims to solve the "pre-existing" problem by dramatically transforming our entire health care system — even though most insured Americans prefer to keep the coverage they have — and by creating an enormous and expensive system of regulations and entitlements. It thus creates even greater risks to the sustainability of private health insurance, with taxpayers ultimately left to pick up the even more expensive costs of over-subsidized, overregulated, and hyper-politicized health care under the PPACA.

High-Risk Pool Alternatives

A different model for a promising national solution can be found in the experience of a number of states. Over the last two decades, they increasingly turned to an approach that does not require a fundamental transformation of the insurance marketplace: the creation of high-risk pools. Unfortunately, these state-level efforts have in most cases been neither sufficiently ambitious nor adequately funded. Those state-run high-risk pools will also be badly undermined and ultimately displaced by the PPACA. But health policy reformers concerned about the problem of pre-existing conditions should consider discarding the PPACA approach to coverage of pre-existing health conditions and replacing it with a system of robust, well-funded high-risk pools.

High-risk pools are basically a policy mechanism for bridging the gap between the high cost of providing insurance to patients with predictably expensive pre-existing health conditions and the comparatively lower premiums those patients can afford. In most states that have established such programs, the pool is administered by a highly regulated, independent nonprofit entity that offers a selection of health-benefit plans. The pool administrator usually contracts out to participating private insurers the work of managing benefits and interacting with customers (e.g., the collection of premiums and the payment of claims). In some states, the risk-pool program is run more directly by the state health or insurance department (which still contracts out most key management functions to private insurers).

The high-risk pool programs cover people who apply after first trying to get insurance elsewhere but are denied coverage, or who receive only unaffordable coverage offers. The program's administrators first must determine an applicant's eligibility. Common eligibility criteria in the states include (in addition to having been rejected for coverage, based on health reasons, by private insurers) having been refused coverage except at rates exceeding the subsidized premium offered in the state's high-risk pool; having received private coverage offers, but only with restrictive riders or pre-existing condition limitations; the existence of particular medical conditions (like HIV/AIDS, cancer, or diabetes) presumed to result in rejection by health insurers; or being a dependent of a person eligible for high-risk pool coverage. The pools also often cover people who, having maintained continuous coverage under HIPAA rules, need to find new insurance arrangements in the individual market.

Because everyone in the pool has, by definition, a high-risk profile, its average claim costs are necessarily quite high. However, the premiums that eligible individuals pay directly are capped at various levels above standard rates. For remaining costs above those caps, additional premium payments are fully subsidized from various public revenue sources. The core concept is that people should pay only the premiums they can afford, and the difference between those payments and the real cost of insurance will be made up by taxpayers.

In theory, high-risk pools should not only help provide coverage for people with pre-existing conditions, but also lower premium costs in the rest of the insurance marketplace. The pools essentially remove more (if not all) of the uncertainty involved in covering the least-healthy consumers from the cost structure financed by normal premium payments. When the predictably high-cost "tail" of the health cost distribution is taken out of the equation, premiums go down and become more attractive for lower-risk customers, thus further expanding the pool of premium payers (and again lowering costs for everyone else).[12]

The first high-risk pools were instituted in Minnesota and Connecticut in 1976. When the PPACA was enacted in March 2011, 35 states were operating some version of high-risk pools. In 2008, approximately 200,000 people were enrolled in state high-risk pools; the average length of enrollment was three years (about 20 to 25% of enrollees leave each year), and the average age of those enrolled was 49. The premium costs that enrollees in these high-risk pools must pay are generally capped at levels between 125% and 150% of standard market rates (although some states — like Texas and South Carolina — go up to 200% or higher, while others — like Minnesota — cap them below 125% for some categories of beneficiaries).[13]

Premium revenue contributed by enrollees amounted to just over half (54%) of total high-risk pool funding in 2008; the rest came from a combination of assessments on private insurance carriers (23.2%), state general revenues (5%), state tobacco taxes (2.2%), and federal grants (1.7%). (A total of about $286 million had been awarded to states to establish new high-risk pools or subsidize existing ones under a federal program in operation since 2002.) The less transparent categories of "other assessments" (7.4%) and "other" (6.3%) comprised the rest of the funding sources.

Although high-risk pools have helped hundreds of thousands of Americans, they still fall far short of meeting the needs they are meant to address. In addition to the large differences among the state plans in terms of eligibility rules, benefit design, premium prices, subsidies, and financing, there are also huge discrepancies in effectiveness.

The pools' main shortcoming almost always stems from the large mismatch between the number of people who need them and the amount of money made available to subsidize them. Just how many people might face pre-existing condition exclusions and might benefit from high-risk pools is not a simple question, but several serious attempts to arrive at a reliable set of estimates have been made in recent years.

In a 2001 survey by the Department of Health and Human Services, respondents were asked if they had "ever been denied health insurance because of poor health." The data collected indicate that about 2 million people might be eligible for enrollment in high-risk pools.[14]

In a different study, using 2006 data, the Government Accountability Office determined roughly the percentage of uninsured individuals who had at least one chronic health condition, and then applied it to census estimates of the average number of uninsured people in each state with an existing high-risk pool. (The aim was to get a sense of how many more people might be covered by such pools if they were available to all who needed them.) The GAO concluded that as many as 4 million Americans could be covered by more generously funded high-risk pools — 20 times the number now covered.[15]

More recently, University of Pennsylvania health economist Mark Pauly looked at data about the number of people with chronic health conditions whose expected medical expenses are more than twice the national average. He first estimated the total nationwide high-risk group at around 4% of the under-65 population, excluding people receiving Medicaid — a number in the low millions. But Pauly ultimately concluded that the number of people who were both high-risk and looking for coverage in the individual market at any given point was far lower — on the order of tens of thousands.[16]

Regardless of the particular sources or estimating methods, which all have their limitations, it is clear that the demand for premium assistance among those with high expected health costs substantially exceeded the pre-PPACA financial capacity of then-operating state high-risk pools.

If one assumes that the higher ranges of these estimates are correct, what would it cost to use high-risk pools to cover as many as 2 million to 4 million people? For an initial assessment, let's start with the 2008 average subsidized cost of $4,341 per pool enrollee — the amount states contributed to their programs beyond the premiums paid by enrollees.[17] If we assume that as many as 4 million more people might need (and seek) high-risk pool coverage, the annual cost of public subsidies could be as high as $17 billion. Other variables might include whether the new enrollees are likely to be somewhat less costly than current ones (since their health status might be less dire); whether benefits and cost-sharing levels are more or less generous than under recent high-risk pool coverage;

and whether additional income-based subsidies for enrollees are included. Within a fairly wide range of uncertainty regarding likely levels of enrollment, a reasonable initial estimate based on the above assumptions, could equal as much as $15 billion to $20 billion per year for a comprehensive set of high-risk pool programs.

Given that large price tag and the fiscal stresses most state governments continue to experience after a deep recession, it should be no surprise that state-based pools have been underfunded and closed off to many potential beneficiaries. Indeed, the most common complaint about pre-PPACA high-risk pools was that their coverage remained too expensive and too limited. Most state pools offered comprehensive insurance benefits (of the sort that most people in employer-based coverage receive), generally with 20% co-insurance, although they tended to impose higher deductibles (and some had lower lifetime-coverage limits) than private insurers. Furthermore, to control costs, all pre-PPACA state high-risk pools imposed pre-existing condition exclusion periods — ranging from two months to one year — for enrollees who forfeited (or never accrued) portability rights under HIPAA.[18] Facing fiscal pressures, many states were also not aggressive in trying to boost high-risk pool enrollment through advertising and outreach to potential enrollees; nor were they eager to pay commissions as generous as those paid by private insurers to insurance agents who brought in customers.

In short, the lack of adequate financing still left far too many potential high-risk beneficiaries with inferior options — and sometimes no options — for health-care coverage. So while high-risk pools offer a plausible and promising conceptual model for covering people with pre-existing conditions, their real-life implementation has (at least to date) left much room for improvement.

Advocates of pro-market health-care reform should therefore urge states to properly design and operate high-risk pools, and should call on the federal government to properly fund them. Such pools would offer an effective, yet far less expensive and intrusive, approach to the problem of covering pre-existing conditions than the tack taken by the PPACA. Well before the latter's most important provisions take effect in 2014, the law's poorly designed attempt to construct a short-term version of high-risk pools–either under federal guidance to the states or more direct administration by the federal government — has already faltered.

High-risk pools have tended not to be popular with liberal health care reformers, who would prefer deep government involvement in the inner workings of the insurance system.[19] The health care plan Barack Obama offered when he ran for president in 2008 therefore made no room for the pools. Obama campaign surrogates and supporters were critical, if not dismissive, of Senator John McCain's proposal to use such pools as part of a broader reform of the health care system.[20] President Obama and congressional Democrats remained disdainful of high-risk pools when they began to develop their health care legislation in 2009, relying instead on mandates and subsidies for private insurance — along with a substantial expansion of Medicaid — to move toward universal insurance coverage. The new law includes an outright ban on insurers' excluding pre-existing conditions from coverage, and on insurers' requiring people with higher health risks to pay higher premiums (older enrollees would still pay more than younger ones, up to a point).[21]

But the PPACA's approach to insurance coverage for Americans with pre-existing conditions (and everyone else, too) differs from previous state efforts in one important way: Starting in 2014, health-insurance coverage will no longer be voluntary; almost every American must either carry insurance or pay a fine. In theory, mandating insurance enrollment is supposed to prevent the young and healthy from fleeing the marketplace when their premiums are increased to cover higher-cost cases (thus preventing any regulation-induced meltdown of private insurance markets). But many insurance experts argue that the insurance mandate — which charges a much smaller penalty to almost everyone who fails to comply with this individual mandate than their far greater cost to purchase qualified insurance coverage — will not work as designed, because too many young and healthy people will still choose to stay out of the system. For them, it could make financial sense to go without coverage, particularly when the PPACA would allow them to enroll later as needed, without any additional restrictions on their access to coverage. The Obama plan could therefore bring about much of the same dysfunctional regulatory cycle that previously relied on guaranteed issue and community rating restrictions in state-level initiatives and produced disappointing, if not dismal, results.

Furthermore, as part of a political ploy to mask the PPACA's full cost and keep the 10-year Congressional Budget Office score for the proposed bill below $1 trillion, the new insurance system and expensive taxpayer subsidies to finance it will not go into effect until 2014. Democrats knew they had to offer something to voters on the pre-existing condition front in the interim. To fill this gap, they resorted to the mechanism they had long derided: high-risk pools. The final law required that high-risk pools for people with pre-existing conditions be established within three months of the law's enactment (early July 2010) and operate until January 1, 2014, when the new insurance rules and subsidies would go into effect.

These high-risk pool provisions were hastily cobbled together as an afterthought to PPACA's other, more sweeping reforms. Their basic structure and the early experience in implementing them remain likely to exacerbate, rather than resolve, the problems faced by states and patients. For procedural and political reasons, Democratic congressional leaders had to adopt the Senate's sketchy version of high-risk pools included within a bill originally passed in December 2009. The new pools would operate very differently from the high-risk pools already established in 35 states that were designed to operate with even more limited resources. The new state pools under PPACA rules cannot allow any exclusions or waiting periods for coverage of pre-existing conditions. Age-based premium variation must be compressed. Cost-sharing is restricted. Most importantly, enrollees can only be charged standard rates. Even the House version of high-risk pools passed in November 2009 (HR 3952) allowed premiums to be as high as 125 percent of the prevailing standard rate in a state's individual market (still the low end of what most existing state pools charged).

Those final rules were a significant departure from the practice of all then-current state-based high-risk pools. Age-based premium rating would be more constrained, and insurers in the new risk pools would be required to pay at least 65% of the costs of covered medical treatments and procedures (clashing with some states' established practices that required patients to pay for a greater portion of their treatments). In effect, the PPACA aimed to impose on the high-risk pools many of the restrictions it will place on insurance coverage, benefits, and premiums in the new health exchanges to be established in 2014 under the new law — but three and a half years before the latter are fully drafted and implemented.

However, both the earlier Senate and House versions of the health reform law, as well as the final one, tried to limit high-risk pool eligibility to those individuals already uninsured for at least six months. The House bill did establish somewhat better-defined "medically eligible" categories for such subsidized coverage (previously denied private coverage, offered such coverage with condition limits, or offered coverage at rates above those for high-risk pool coverage within the previous six months) than simply the Senate's looser requirement in section 1101(d) of what became the final law's language that an enrollee also must have a pre-existing condition as determined by the guidance of the HHS Secretary.

By most initial estimates, the law also appeared to underfund substantially the high-risk pools it requires, authorizing a total of only $5 billion for three and a half years of operation. The PPACA provisions for high-risk pools tried to get around the law's budget limitations by authorizing the newly mandated pools -- in section 1101(g) (4) -- to "stop taking applications for participation in the program...to comply with the funding limitation" when the money runs out; it also vaguely empowers the HHS secretary – in section 1101(g) (2) -- to make "such adjustments as are necessary" to eliminate any deficit in the program during any fiscal year. In addition, the law suppresses potential demand for new high-risk pool coverage by limiting eligibility to people who have already been uninsured for six months. Merely having a pre-existing condition, and being turned down for coverage because of it, is not enough to gain access to subsidized coverage in the new high-risk pools. Nor can one gain admission to the new pools if one is already enrolled in an existing state high-risk pool but facing higher premiums with greater cost-sharing. After all, people in these circumstances are not already "uninsured for six months."

In other words, the Secretary of Health and Human Services was first authorized to determine which pre-existing conditions make a potential enrollee eligible for federal high-risk pool coverage — and then, if budget funds ran short, was required to figure out how to avoid actually providing that person with the promised health-care coverage. The results seemed easy to foresee: waiting periods, benefit limits, and rationing of care — all the practices for which the new law's champions attack the private insurance industry and already-operating state high-risk pools.

In April 2010, the chief actuary of the Department of Health and Human Services released a cost projection for the new program, predicting that the $5 billion the law allocates for three-and-a-half years of high-risk pools would in fact be exhausted in the program's first or second year. The actuary estimated that only 375,000 people shut out of insurance elsewhere would obtain health care coverage through the high-risk pools — a number that would fall far short of the 2 to 4 million people in the targeted population.[22]

However, early experience under the new risk pools (soon relabeled "pre-existing condition insurance plans" by image makers at HHS) turned out quite differently. As of April 30, 2011, enrollment in the renamed Pre-Existing Condition Insurance Plans (PCIPs) program was a little over 20,000 and more recent Obama administration estimates set the figure around 34,000.[23] Only twenty-seven states elected to administer a PCIP for their residents. Twenty-three other states and the District of Columbia chose to allow HHS to administer such plans. In any case, enrollment has fallen dramatically short of expectations, even after HHS redesigned its PCIP rules to lower premiums even more and to make it easier for applicants to document that they had a pre-existing condition.

One might ask whether flawed design and enrollment assumptions for the new high-risk pools by the Obama administration and its congressional allies initially reflected reluctance to acknowledge the total cost to fully fund them on the scale that was commensurate with what those same parties claimed was a much larger pre-existing condition problem that justified other provisions of the PPACA. Simply funding a potentially robust PCIP solution would diminish the rationale for controlling even more of the private health insurance market through sweeping regulation, tight premium controls, and complex cross-subsidies.

Or did the more limited funding dedicated to PCIPs under the law reflect the tacit acknowledgement that the actual pre-existing condition problem had been greatly exaggerated?[24] Most likely, it represented a combination of both, along with the perceived budgetary imperative to suppress demand for such high-risk pool coverage and stretch out the limited taxpayer funding at least until broader coverage expansions under Medicaid and the new exchanges kicked in after the end of 2013.

A July 2011 report by the Government Accountability Office suggested that the primary reasons for lower-than-expected enrollment were the statutory requirement that applicants be uninsured for at least six months, affordability concerns, and lack of awareness of the PCIP program.[25] However, the most likely explanation is that the estimated size of the population denied coverage due to a pre-existing condition is much smaller in practice than the inexact estimates of various national surveys suggest and that the primary reason for lack of coverage is its unaffordable cost to potential purchasers *in general* (rather than just to those with particular high-risk conditions). Offers of free or very heavily subsidized coverage might encourage more substantial enrollment (leaving aside their budgetary costs), but the broader affordability problem is much greater than the slightly higher surcharges in premiums facing most individuals with pre-existing conditions.

High-Risk Pools that Won't Run Dry

A better solution should begin with *redefining* the problem. We should avoid the temptation of trying to achieve multiple policy objectives with a single tool, which results in mission creep and failure to target scarce resources more effectively and sustainably. True high-risk pools should be limited to covering the most likely, highest-risk individuals, as identified before the fact of enrollment. They don't work as well as a mechanism for subsidizing the health care costs of low-income individuals more broadly, or for covering the uninsured in general. They address a problem that is real, but apparently much smaller in its own terms than most observers previously have estimated. However, the issue of costly pre-existing conditions that might limit access to private health insurance for individuals presenting such risks has been exaggerated and exploited as a rationale to advance a much broader political agenda to control private insurance coverage and pricing for everyone else much more extensively.

The present and future failings of the PPACA's high-risk pool component are functions of its careless design, not an indictment of the fundamental concept. A more effective solution to our enduring problem in dealing with insurance coverage of some individuals with high-risk/high-cost health conditions remains a better-designed, robustly funded, and more narrowly targeted system of state high-risk pools — not the new law's massive and misguided transformation of American health care. The guiding principle for a more effective approach is straightforward: Americans who stay in continuous insurance coverage should not be penalized for developing costly health conditions. Several key policy components to achieve this objective include:

1. Congress must fix several of the flaws in HIPAA noted above. Workers leaving job-based plans for the individual market should be able to do so without being penalized for failing to exhaust their COBRA rights. If a worker moves directly from an employer-provided plan to an individual policy, that individual should not be denied coverage based on a pre-existing condition.

2. States should impose limits (based on broader federal guidelines) on underwriting for people who move from the employer-based market to the individual market. Those limits probably should involve capping the premiums charged to high-risk customers at some fixed level above their standard rates, regardless of income, and then having the state government provide supplemental sliding-scale subsidies to the poor. The aim is to allow insurers to take higher health risks into account when calculating premiums, while also ensuring that people with expensive health conditions are not completely priced out of the market. (Identifying people at very high risks could also help insurers to better

tailor health care interventions in order to encourage these customers to change their behavior and lower their risks over time.) Individuals anticipating more expensive health care could and should pay somewhat *more* than others to handle them (i.e., higher premiums and more cost sharing), but with some realistic and equitable ceilings on just how much is too much and guidelines for when public subsidies should step in.

3. The gap between a customer's contribution and the actual cost of insuring that individual must be bridged with taxpayer dollars through high-risk pool programs in the states. These programs must be funded sufficiently in order to function properly. With state budgets overdrawn and overstretched for several more years to come, the reality is that such initial funding will have to come from Washington in the form of a series of modestly generous, but capped, annual appropriations. Capping the amounts would help head off the dangers of open-ended entitlement incentives to overspend, and a switch to state matching funds should be reconsidered in later years. One overlooked way to find most of the funds needed — in places other than the emptying pockets of federal taxpayers – would be to redirect some of the hundreds of billions of dollars in new insurance subsidies scheduled for later years in other portions of the PPACA (for higher-income Medicaid expansions and health exchange coverage) and help those in the greatest need first. Given the recent mistaken estimates of the likely costs of such a program, this funding should start at a more conservative level. Only after the program has undergone the necessary trial and error of implementation and practice — thus providing a better sense of the pools' actual needs and costs — should lawmakers re-examine the funding commitments.

4. The new risk pools themselves must be structured to prevent participating private insurers from dumping unwanted (but not truly high-risk) customers into the public-subsidy system. For example, suppose that an insurer believes that an applicant's health status argues for charging that applicant a premium higher than a given threshold for subsidy assistance at, let's assume, 1.5 times the standard rate. In that

case, the insurer should be allowed to direct the customer to the high-risk pool program in that person's state once the initial private insurance premium quoted for coverage is above that level. The job of determining eligibility for the subsidy should be contracted out by the state to a neutral third party with experience in medical insurance underwriting, with private insurers collaborating to determine in advance the criteria for high-risk selection. If the third party finds no basis for designating the applicant an unusually high risk, the insurer seeking the evaluation would be required to take the applicant at no more than the maximum rate of (in this example) 1.5 times the standard premium. (And if the insurer makes failed claims too often, it would pay additional penalty fees to the state — thus discouraging so-called excessive risk dumping.) But if the insurer's application is deemed valid, the state would subsidize the individual's high premium in its high-risk pool program, taking into account the enrollee's income and other resources.

5. Properly structured high-risk pools also have the potential to concentrate resources and attention on the most important, highest-cost cases. They could identify and gather together exactly those individuals who need additional disease management, navigational assistance, and specialized care from centers of excellence. In addition, initial reliance on private insurers' screening and designation of high-risk applicants would retain risk-reduction incentives for both insurers and patients, while tempering the bureaucratic rigidities of complex risk-adjustment calculation.

6. Insurers participating in the individual market would need to offer coverage without a new risk assessment to anyone who has maintained a private insurance policy for some minimum period when applying for a new one. This would mean that market entrants would face a risk evaluation only once; they would then have the right to renew their policies at the same rate class from any licensed insurer. This approach also would provide strong incentives to maintain insurance coverage to avoid the risk of becoming subject to higher risk-based premiums or coverage exclusions based on health status in the future – as a

less intrusive but still effective alternative to the PPACA's individual mandate to purchase insurance.

Finally, when these reforms are first implemented, there will need to be a one-time enrollment period to allow people who have fallen through the cracks over the years to re-establish their rights by maintaining continuous coverage. Those who have forfeited their coverage would get at least one more fair chance to become insured under the new rules (though perhaps at higher rates than those who had not forfeited their rights). But once this initial enrollment window closed, everyone would know that people who remain continuously insured are protected, and that those who choose not to become insured have taken a risk of becoming subject to pre-existing condition exclusions or facing higher risk-based insurance premiums in the future.

This approach to covering pre-existing conditions would not be inexpensive. But its price would be minimal compared to that of the new health care law's extensive web of regulations and subsidies. Using high-risk pools to cover people who are uninsured because of pre-existing medical conditions would head off the transfer of even more power over our health care system to bureaucrats in Washington. It would enlist states in a partnership to provide necessary coverage to their most vulnerable citizens. Moreover, it would not disrupt insurance arrangements that are working well for the vast majority of Americans, and would leave in place the many other protections already available to people in the much larger employer-based insurance market.

The PPACA version of federally-guided high-risk pools represents a half-hearted and misguided attempt to help those who need the most assistance. The new pools are off to a rocky start and remain destined to disappoint because, like many other provisions of the overall law, they promise far more than they can deliver. Critics should seize the opportunity to change the game by replacing this flawed structure with one that actually could work, a structure that is based on less federal regulation, more consumer choice, and better-targeted financing. Solving the problem of covering Americans with pre-existing conditions does not require a massive transformation of America's health care system. The PPACA will increase costs, raise taxes, displace millions of the happily insured, create a new entitlement, and undermine our private insurance sector. A more targeted version of high-risk pools run by the states, with a firmer foundation of sufficient federal financial assistance, can illustrate best what it means to replace, and not just repeal, the flawed prescription of the new health law for health policy change.

3

Choice and Competition in Health Care

Tom Miller

Consumer-Directed Regulation of Insurance at the State Level

One-size-fits-all approaches to health insurance regulation are prone to limiting consumer choices and imposing excessive regulatory burdens, whether they operate at the national level, particularly through the PPACA, or at the state level, through traditional state regulation of fully insured insurance products and their carriers. Limiting the size and scope of an exclusive franchise for health insurance regulation to state boundary lines does not by itself promise to make it either more accountable or market sensitive. Empowering consumers with a greater diversity of affordable health benefits choices will require exposing exclusive state health care regulation based on geography to competition from other potential brands of regulation offered in other states.

The traditional role of states in health insurance regulation has remained significant in recent decades, but it has been increasingly limited to the small group and individual insurance markets. The growth of self-insured health benefits plans sponsored and financed by almost all large employers and many mid-sized ones has reduced the overall reach of state regulation. The Employee Retirement Income Security Act (ERISA), enacted by Congress in 1974, generally preempts most state regulation of employers offering such plans. Until enactment of the Affordable Care Act, it also ensured that, with a few exceptions, the thrust of federal health policy toward employer-sponsored insurance would tilt toward a less prescriptive regulatory approach that encouraged greater flexibility in health benefits design, financing, and administration.

On the other hand, employers and workers in smaller firms (particularly those with fewer than 50 employees) have had to bear the brunt of excessive health insurance regulation in many states. Smaller firms generally are unable to self-insure and gain ERISA preemption protection from state benefit mandates, restrictions on rating and underwriting, and other regulatory burdens. Although insurers and consumers of individual market products also are subject to state regulation, the more fragile nature of that smaller market has generally limited the degree to which the tightest state restrictions on risk rating, mandated benefits, and insurer practices apply to individual market products.

In general, increased state regulation in recent decades has raised the cost of health insurance and limited the range of benefits package design. A wide assortment of small group regulatory measures imposed by many states during the 1990s failed to improve levels of insurance coverage and, in some cases, priced low-risk consumers out of the small group market. Various state government regulatory attempts to force low-risk insureds to subsidize high-cost insureds through devices like modified community rating and guaranteed issue often were counterproductive; they triggered premium spirals that drove younger, healthier, and lower-income workers out of the voluntary insurance market. Many states also increased the number and scope of mandates to cover specific types of benefits and providers, further increasing the added regulatory cost contribution to rising insurance premiums. Excessive state regulation at times has also encouraged exit from the market by smaller insurers, increased consolidation in the insurance industry, and distorted market-based prices. In other words, state health insurance regulation more often than not has been at least part of the problem, rather than part of the solution.[1]

Competition among the States in Health Insurance Regulation

A better alternative for addressing patterns of state-based regulatory failure is not a new round of heavy-handed federal rule-making or pre-emption (such as in the PPACA), but rather facilitation of competitive federalism — revitalized state competition in health insurance regulation that reaches across geographic boundary lines. The most successful model for such competitive federalism involves corporate law and the business of corporate charters, in which Delaware has specialized for many decades and excelled by consistently producing benefits to its "customers" — investors.[2] More limited examples can be found in the traditional dual banking regulatory model for federal and state chartering of depository institutions, regional compacts to facilitate interstate banking in the 1980s, and entry of out-of-state surplus lines insurance carriers to address market shortages.

Such regulatory competition would limit the excesses of geographically based monopoly regulation. Currently, insurance consumers (at least in the non-self-insured market) are subject to a single state government's "brand" of insurance product regulation. Solely by virtue of where they live, they are stuck with the entire bundle of their home state's rules. Short of physically moving to another state, they are unable to choose ex ante the type of health insurance regulatory regime they might prefer and need as part of the insurance package they purchase.

Competitive federalism could facilitate diversity and experimentation in health insurance regulatory approaches. It would discipline the tendency of insurance regulation to promote inefficient wealth transfers and promote individual choice over collective decisions driven by interest group politics.[3] In short, it would improve the quality of health insurance regulation, thereby enhancing the availability and affordability of health insurance products. Insurers facing market competition across state lines would have strong incentives to disclose and adhere to policies that encouraged consumers to buy their products and services. Employers and individuals purchasing insurance would migrate to state regulatory regimes that did not impose unwanted mandates but, instead, fit the needs of their consumers. State lawmakers would become more sensitive to the potential for insurer exit. At a minimum, interstate regulatory competition would provide an escape valve from arbitrary or discriminatory regulatory policies imposed at either state or federal levels.

How to Do It

Several political shortcuts to the reform of state-based health insurance regulation would be counterproductive. They include broad-based federal preemption of state activity, which might achieve short-term political objectives in the near term but fail to sustain them structurally over time. Optional federal chartering in which health insurers can bypass state regulation for a single federal regulator and build a single national market for their products ignores the danger of creating long-term incentives for a new and bigger monopoly regulator that only will recreate past problems on a larger, even less-accountable, scale.

Key design requirements for regulatory competition in health insurance would include:

1. *Clear Regulatory Primacy.* Only one sovereign (the lead, or primary, state regulator) has jurisdiction over a particular set of health insurance transactions, and its law controls the primary regulatory components of the regime governing them. Other "secondary" states provide regulatory reciprocity (also known as the "principle of mutual recognition" in the European Union), by respecting and enforcing that state's insurance charter and its accompanying rules. Such reciprocity works through private arbitrage of jurisdictional competition, rather than politically mandated harmonization that suppresses competition.

2. *Domicile-based Regulatory Choice.* Health insurers can choose their statutory domicile, or otherwise determine the applicable forum and applicable law that governs transactions, and make it part of the purchasing option they present to consumers. Insurers and their

consumers can exercise the right of free exit: they can vote with their feet and their pocketbooks. Insurers can choose their domiciles, the markets where they prefer to operate, and the bundle of laws and regulations attached to the products they sell. They can relocate to alternate jurisdictions at relatively low cost. Consumers may choose not only the state in which they live but also the legal rules attached to the insurance products they buy.

3. *Primary State Incentives and Responsibilities*: States must receive some benefits, such as tax revenues, from competing in the production of specific laws and regulations that reduce insurers' business costs and increase the value of insurance products. Conversely, states also must feel within their own borders a sufficient number of negative consequences of the regulatory regimes they choose to adopt and export to consumers in other states. For these reasons, a secondary state regulator should not be able to have exclusive rights to premium tax revenue collected from an out-of-state insurer selling policies in that state (although some legislative proposals for interstate competition in state regulation of individual market insurers require this).[4] Such revenue either should be shared with a primary state regulator, or allocated on the basis of the actual regulatory costs incurred by the respective states. In addition, eligible policies regulated by primary states must actually be offered for sale there, and it may be necessary to ensure that at least a minimum percentage of the sales revenue of an insurer they regulate is derived from such primary state transactions. Primary states should also be required to contribute their pro rata share of any secondary state assessments for high-risk pool coverage or other mechanisms to ensure HIPAA-guaranteed access to care for their vulnerable populations.

4. *Thorough Disclosure and Informed Choice.* Competition among insurers to attract the marginal and more informed consumer must operate to protect other consumers who are less aware or informed of the particular regulatory regime linked to their insurance arrangements. Rather than present a single set of contract terms on an all-or-nothing basis, insurers

can offer consumers a menu of alternative policies that are priced to reflect different regulatory approaches.

5. *Multi-State Solvency Arrangements*. Solvency regulation should remain decentralized and kept at the state level to avoid federal domination over other regulation in the name of protecting consumers and taxpayers. Regulatory competition for insurance product design, pricing, and pooling could be accommodated within the current state-based guaranty fund system in a manner that limits an individual state's opportunities to impose costs on other jurisdictions.

Several mechanisms or paths could lead to vigorous interstate competition in health insurance regulation. One approach advanced several times over the last decade has involved federal legislation starts with providing the option of setting an "insurer domicile" rule, in place of a "site of transaction" rule, for determining applicable state law and regulatory authority. The first such example was introduced in 2002 by then-Representative Ernest Fletcher (R-KY). The "State Cooperative Health Care Access Plan Act" (H.R. 4170) would have authorized a health insurer offering an insurance policy in one primary state (the primary location for the insurer's business) to offer the same policy type in a secondary state. The product, rate, and form filing laws of the primary state would apply to the same health insurance policy offered in the secondary state.

Subsequent variations of this approach have been refined in proposed legislation by then-Representative John Shadegg (R-AZ) — "Health Care Choice Act" (H.R. 4460, 2007), Representative Tom Price (R-GA) — "The Empowering Patients First Act" (H.R. 3400, 2009), and, most recently, Representative Marsha Blackburn (R-TN) – "Health Care Choice Act" (H.R. 371, 2011).

These latter bills have limited this option to the market for individual health insurance, unlike the original Fletcher bill, which also covered the small group market, even though the potential pool of interested purchasers is much larger and state regulatory burdens involving rating restrictions and mandated benefits actually are greatest in the latter market. They also focus more narrowly on providing ways to reduce the excess costs of state-mandated insurance benefits, rather than reducing overall state regulatory burdens of all kinds. In any case, the political sale on Capitol Hill for such bills has never been closed even at the congressional committee markup stage, as defenders of current mandates point to anecdotal evidence of potential patient "victims" who might lose access to disease-specific benefits coverage required by their home state's insurance laws.

A more modest federal statutory approach might simply set an "insurer domicile" rule, in place of a "site of transaction" rule, for determining applicable state law and regulatory authority as a default setting for multi-state transactions where the respective parties do not otherwise designate operative law.

Another route to interstate competition in insurance regulation might be built on decisions by individual states to grant regulatory due deference to determinations by out-of-state insurance regulators that a particular insurance company is qualified to conduct such business. Once an insurer submitted evidence of good standing in its domestic jurisdiction and (if different) in the jurisdiction where it conducts the largest share of its health insurance business, it would qualify for licensure in the state granting such regulatory deference. Regulators in secondary states would be most likely to treat proof of licensure and good standing in the primary state as prima facie evidence of qualification for licensure in the secondary state, while still requiring additional routine documents, fees, and compliance of the primary state's insurance department with broadly accepted accreditation standards, such as those maintained by the National Association of Insurance Commissioners.

Initially, an individual state's decision to grant regulatory due deference would be similar to a declaration of unilateral free trade in health insurance products. The state would be eliminating or reducing its regulatory restrictions on out-of-state insurance to benefit its citizens and to provide a model for other states to emulate.

Involving Congress in structuring interstate regulatory competition may be necessary to defuse threats of retaliation and exit restrictions by individual state insurance regulators. However, it remains unlikely that Congress would relinquish a great deal of its current and future regulatory authority over health insurance without asking for something in return. For that reason, more of a contractual approach among consenting states would be preferable to the more targeted statutory fixes above that are more likely to require costly political side payments.

Several states have explored legislative offers to authorize sale and purchase of insurance provided by out-of-state insurers. In March 2010, the state of Wyoming authorized such sales, provided for cooperation by its insurance commissioner with other states with consistent insurance laws, and specified legislative intent to pursue a multi-state consortium to enter into reciprocal agreements to reduce health insurance costs through removal of duplicative regulation. In May 2011, the state of Georgia authorized its insurers to offer individual accident and sickness insurance policies to Georgia residents that have been approved for issuance in other states, provided minimum standards for such policies, and allowed insurers authorized to transact insurance in other states to issue individual accident and sickness policies in the state.

Earlier this year, the state of Maine established a process for its residents to purchase individual health insurance from most other New England states (with the exception of Vermont), beginning in 2014. Maine's reciprocity-based approach provides that an insurer approved to sell an individual market health policy in New Hampshire, Massachusetts, Connecticut, or Rhode Island may request certification from Maine insurance regulators to sell the same product there. Eligible out-of-state insurers still must meet Maine's standards for handling consumer grievances and other consumer protections, but their products only need to comply with their own state's benefit mandates and premium rate regulations. Once those out-of-state insurers are approved to conduct business in Maine, Maine's domestic insurers also may choose to offer similar plans in those other participating New England states, provided that the Maine-based insurers comply with those respective states' regulations for benefit mandates and premium rates.[5]

Similar reciprocal agreements among states could be bolstered and expanded through more formal interstate compacts. These contracts between states are authorized under the U.S. Constitution as the equivalent of a treaty between sovereign powers. They require the consent of Congress if they increase the political powers of the contracting states or encroach upon the "just supremacy" of the United States. In other words, Congress must provide consent to (1) agreements that would change the balance of power between the States and the federal government or diminish the latter's power, and (2) to those compacts that would intrude on an area of specific federal authority.[6] Given that most proposed state agreements to facilitate purchasing across state lines would conflict with at least portions of the national scheme of insurance regulation envisioned under the Affordable Care Act, those types of interstate compacts would appear to require congressional approval.

Congressional consent may be granted conditionally upon terms appropriate to the subject and transgressing no constitutional limitations. Opinions by constitutional scholars regarding whether approval by the president also is required remains divided; some argue that any congressional resolution of approval is subject to a presidential veto, but there appears to be no direct court precedent on this issue.[7]

A more ambitious proposal to reassert state governments' role in determining health policy for their citizens involves a far-reaching interstate compact that would replace most federal health care programs, including Medicaid and Medicare, with block grants to the states. A model law version of this Health Care Compact has been approved in four states thus far (Georgia, Oklahoma, Texas, and Missouri), and it remains under consideration in a number of other states.[8] It essentially proposes a grand swap of federal revenue to states in return for the latter taking full responsibility for handling most publicly subsidized health care needs of their home state residents. Although the compact would provide states with much broader discretion in setting the terms of health policy and operating health programs to carry it out, serious challenges and uncertainties remain concerning how sustainable any initial transfer of federal funding would be, the terms of its allocation and distribution, and transitional issues—let alone more basic political opposition to the restructuring of major national health entitlement programs. Enactment of the compact by a substantial number of states (either regionally contiguous ones or a much larger overall majority) and approval by Congress would represent a seminal transformation of respective federal and state roles in current health policy.

Potential Constituencies for Greater Choice and Competition in Insurance Regulation

Even more-limited versions of interstate competition and cooperation in regulating health insurance will require mobilization of political constituencies that see how they need and would benefit from greater choice in types of such state-based regulation. Price-sensitive potential purchasers of individual market health insurance, albeit in a less centrally regulated world than the one envisioned in the PPACA, usually come to mind in this regard; particularly if new taxpayer assistance provided to them for insurance purchases is tied to new rules for subsidy-eligible insurance products that encourage portability and long-term contracts.

Another possible block of customers for competitive federalism-style insurance regulation includes online purchasers of individual insurance. Congress might consider a special carve-out to minimize the growth of new regulatory burdens on this promising channel of distribution. Matching regulatory jurisdiction to an insurer's state of incorporation might simplify the regulatory branding for web-based insurance products. It also would allow an insurer to offer potential online purchasers a more uniform insurance product regardless of where they live, as well as lower marketing and distribution costs that add to total premiums.

A different cohort of future candidates for reinvigorated state regulatory competition might turn out to be large, self-insured, multi-state firms. If the regulatory burdens ahead under the PPACA begin to negate the longstanding advantages of the ERISA preemption by substituting a multitude of new federal mandates on those employer plans, their sponsoring firms still might seek the second-best uniformity of consolidated regulation at the *state* level. Even without as much of a deregulatory haven as ERISA provided in the past, large firms might consider the virtues of linking all their plans to a single, market-friendly, state-based regulatory regime. If state insurance regulatory systems could compete on an interstate basis, the better ones might find a new customer base in multi-state firms seeking consolidated regulation of more fully insured products.

Will Regulatory Competition Improve Health Insurance?

Unfortunately, the special-interest politics of health insurance regulation often means that those states whose residents would benefit the most from jurisdictional competition are the least likely to participate in either interstate compacts or regulatory due deference. Nevertheless, preliminary evidence suggests the potential gains from facilitating a rearrangement of the regulatory deck of cards. One sophisticated analysis of "Consumer Response to a National Marketplace" by Parente et al. concluded that permitting national competition for non-group/individual health insurance has the potential to strengthen competition, reduce prices, and increase demand for such insurance policies.[9]

The authors examined three scenarios for regulatory competition (among the five largest states, among all 50 states, and within four regions) and found significant opportunity to reduce the number of uninsured. Although the best scenario involved competition among all fifty states with one eventual clear winner (a moderate national impact of 8.2 million previously-uninsured gaining coverage), Parente et al. conclude that the most pragmatic positive scenario involves one winner in each regional market, which produces a net increase of 7.4 million newly insured compared to the pre-PPACA status quo. They also observed that states with the highest regulatory burdens would have the greatest movement of individual market insurance purchasers to a less-regulated state. Coverage for the chronically ill was greater in the national marketplace model than in the status quo because it improved access to coverage that was more affordable.

One should be careful not to overstate the potential impact of regulatory competition among states for health insurance. After adjusting for other factors besides state regulation that might influence geographic variation in private health insurance premiums among states (e.g., population health characteristics, per capita income, unemployment rate, small-firm employment, Medicare spending), Mathur concluded that about 12 percent of overall variation in premiums among states may be due to differences in state regulations such as mandated benefits, community rating, and guaranteed issue.[10] The impact of interstate competition will be greatest on states that are regulatory outliers rather than distributed more evenly across all states. Out-of-state insurers also will face market-based difficulty in penetrating new state markets without pre-established provider networks.

Of course, proposing interstate competition in state health insurance regulation also will face predictable "race to the bottom" warnings. However, those who prefer the existing set of choices within the current health insurance regulatory system can continue to use them. Other consumers who believe there are advantages in new and different regulatory approaches should be allowed to try them. Reputational concerns will provide both constraints and incentives for the choice of regulatory regimes by established insurance firms. There is little to be gained on a long-term basis in contracting for a particular set of laws and forums to govern health insurance that many consumers would be likely to know unduly favors insurance sellers over buyers.

Normal competitive pressure would discourage private insurers from repeatedly switching their state insurance regulator on an opportunistic, short-term basis. Insurers would be more likely to issue a credible promise not to remove to another state, in order to reduce doubts about the enforceability of certain provisions of their insurance contracts. By accepting this restriction voluntarily, a private insurance company might improve its market value. Insurers also would tend to incorporate in states that had an established tradition of regulatory stability and in states whose economy was more dependent on the insurance industry.

State regulators could coordinate their law enforcement activities to deal with interstate problems. They also could require compliance with the standards of a centralized body to assist necessary uniformity in certain areas. Or Congress could establish a default rule for enforcement of certain actions (such as those involving consumer fraud or other improper market conduct) that affect consumers in a secondary state but involve insurance policies regulated by a primary state. The rule would authorize insurance regulators in that secondary state to treat the insurer involved as if it were primarily licensed there.

Defenders of the current regulatory structure, advocates for the even more dubious one ahead under the PPACA, and skeptics of regulatory competition need to answer the "compared to what?" challenge. They cannot just assume that a hypothetically perfect, well-designed system of more and more state (or federal) health insurance regulation will materialize in the future. They need to demonstrate its measurable benefits compared to a more decentralized system of regulatory competition — a system much more likely to deliver the contractual assurances, services, and features for which buyers are willing to pay. The real goal is better regulation, not no regulation at all. Insurance regulators, too, should meet more of a competitive market test. After all, too many states have already been running a different race to the bottom — in terms of resulting outcomes for health care costs, coverage, choices, and competition — with too much regulation. The losers end up uninsured — because they can't afford coverage, or refuse to overpay for it, or cannot find something else they prefer. The race to the "market top" needs a full field of state regulators running in each other's markets.

Improving Health Care Transparency

Increasing choice and competition in health insurance is necessary, but not sufficient, to improve the health care options available to consumers. They also need better choices in who delivers their health care and better information about how well that is done. The primary problems with our health care delivery system do not involve quality as much as cost and value. U.S. patients receive a lot of beneficial medical services, but they may carry high costs, vary unpredictably in quality, and too often fail to reflect good value. Health care frequently is dispensed and received within a complex, fragmented delivery system that lacks sufficient transparency to allow its participants to make sense of what really matters and what is going on. We often just don't know enough about what works and who performs better, if not best. The system still lacks sufficient data, effective measures, and standards to assess the value of health care treatment options and choose health care providers. Even when such information exists, it is not widely available or usable at the consumer level.

Substantial spillover effects could flow from not necessarily more or perfect, but at least better, information about the value of health care services. As we know in most other sectors of the economy, more transparent and usable information strengthens competition and improves the overall level of services. Apart from demand-side factors involving patients and other purchasers, there could be positive effects within the physician and hospital communities on the supply side if they know that they are not doing as well as some of their peers according to respected measures of quality (and, one might hope, measures of cost and value, too).

The objective of achieving greater information transparency in health care is saluted by almost everyone but delivered by too few parties. What can states do?

States should work to sharpen and enhance the tools they have at hand, rather than overpromise and underperform again. They should focus on basic blocking and tackling – enhancing the "public goods" production of aggregated data from health care transactions that supply the raw material from which others can derive more refined measures of all-in costs, health outcomes, patient experience, and relative performance by providers.

Some states have made modest progress in simpler pricing transparency measures, which produce summarized indicators of the relative prices charged by different providers for discreet medical procedures and unbundled health care services.[11] However, this falls well short of what patients and payers really need to know — the overall cost per episode of care. It's one thing to know the individualized list price for a procedure; it's another thing to know what it means over the entire continuum of care. This is particularly true for chronic conditions involving multiple providers whose individual contributions might not be well coordinated.

Other states fall short by reporting only average or median "charges" (but not what is actually paid under negotiated contract prices) for various hospital services. Even reporting of the total amounts that hospitals receive from all payers still may fail to include reporting of separately billed charges for related services by physicians and other professionals during inpatient stays or outpatient visits.

The state of New Hampshire probably has made the greatest progress in reporting to the public the bundled cost of 31 common health care services, which includes provider-specific estimates of the overall costs of both hospital/ facility and physician payments made by both insurers and patients. The state's Health Cost web site began reporting in 2007 on what it learned from claims data collected from all commercial health insurers doing business in New Hampshire. The site provides estimates of expected out-of-pocket costs as well as total costs, broken down by location, insurance status, and insurance carrier. But even in this case, an initial assessment by outside researchers several years ago suggested that the information did not yet appear to be used widely by consumers or have any significant impact on price variation for the same services across different providers and places of care within state health care markets.[12] Limiting factors include the lack of strong financial incentives for many consumers with comprehensive health insurance (and modest cost-sharing expenses) to focus on total costs, increased concentration in health care provider markets and greater resulting pricing power, and geographic market segmentation.

State government institutions have not demonstrated any particularly greater comparative advantage in making more refined and sophisticated assessments of health care value, but their role in paying health care bills, administering health benefits programs, and assembling claims transactions data could contribute greatly to improving the scope and predictive power of efforts by other parties to do so. States generally run two of the largest health care programs in their region – a state Medicaid program and health insurance plans for state government workers. Most of them also are involved in guiding, if not directly operating, an all-payer claims database in their state. So they already possess a large supply of underlying data about health care costs, quality, and value in their market areas, but they generally fail to do much with it to help generate more useful and usable information for health care purchasers and providers.

Aggregation of as much health care data as can be accurately and securely derived from multiple sources is a key early step in the process of developing a more transparent health care system. Such data – whether from administrative processing of claims, medical charts, prescription drug transactions, clinical lab findings, patient registries, or electronic health records – needs to be collected just once, but then used often. While other efforts continue at the federal level to help make more provider-identifiable Medicare data available to qualified intermediaries that can best assess its meaning and to substantially increase the adoption rate and meaningful use of electronic health information tools, states can make an important contribution to the data collection and data sharing process.

Much may depend on the composition of a particular state's overall health care system and the sophistication and capabilities of its current all-payer claims database (APCD) before presuming how large a role in improving and expanding health care transparency the latter can play. (APCDs are usually created by state mandate and generally rely on data derived from various medical claims, along with eligibility and provide files, from private and public payers.) Although some states have created various types of hospital report cards on cost and quality or web portals with price and quality information ranging from health insurance options to select medical treatments, the assumed scope, scale, and predictive power of their respective APCDs can easily be overestimated. The current limits of the billing and discharge records on which they generally rely falls short of the type of patient-identifiable clinical information or data on health care outcomes that some policymakers, providers, payers, and patients envision. Lag times between initial data collection and its release to other users can limit real-time analysis of cost and utilization patterns. The costs to collect more comprehensive information about all health care delivered in a state may exceed the likely payoff. And data that travels too far from its originating source may be prone to misinterpretation. Other potential data sources such as self-funded health plans and negotiated hospital charges subject to contractual "gag clauses" may remain outside the reach of state-level APCDs.

However, more energetic and imaginative states can use APCDs to improve understanding of the overall health of their citizens, such as rates of disease and diagnoses and even underlying causes of morbidity. One perennial limiting factor is that this data information is an important source of power; hence, some parties are not eager to pool and share it. Recent expansion of the Agency for Healthcare Research and Quality's Healthcare Cost and Utilization Project (HCUP) suggests some additional ways to merge and synthesize state APCD data into more useful measures of health care effectiveness and efficiency at both the system and provider levels. Greater use of initial federal grant support to enhance the clinical content of state-level administrative claims data (such as by requiring that key "present on admission" indicators be included in hospital claims records, and linking hospital-based claims data to other laboratory services data sources) should be pursued by states looking to improve the information base for their patients, payers, and providers.

However, state APCDs should first determine which health policy questions their resources and skills can answer effectively before assuming they can do so. Instead of focusing too much on facilitating more elusive, long-term evaluations of the clinical effectiveness of particular treatments, they might start with more tangible measurement and reporting of the relative costs of more routine and frequent health care services, the actual out-of-pocket costs that consumers are likely to face in their own particular insurance plan, and how patients themselves evaluate their care experience with different health providers.

We cannot measure everything, let alone measure it well. Information is not cost-free. And because it often represents sources of power and profit, it may not always be pooled and shared readily. But working within the constraints of existing data sources, improved measurement and reporting at the state level could help set reasonable minimum thresholds for measurement validity, establish baseline standards that provide sufficient consistency but don't stifle further innovation, and facilitate payer-provider collaboration on second-best consensus approaches that will help move us beyond the end of the beginning of performance measurement. Such a "best available" measurement approach has driven measurement and performance improvement in other sectors of the economy. It would be vastly preferable to remaining in the dark about performance variation until more exacting levels of statistical precision can be met.

Better-designed provider-level measurement can make the cost containment tools of differential reimbursement, high-performance tiered networks, value-based benefit design, clinical re-engineering, and the responsible choices they offer more visible and effective.[13] It can also begin to construct a model of state health care regulation that relies more on providing useful information to consumers instead of simply mandating or limiting their choices. This change in mindset on regulatory reform and transparency would prove to be a powerful agent to foster greater choice and competition in health care.

4

Taking Medicaid Off Steroids

Tom Miller

The PPACA puts about 16 million low-income Americans into the Medicaid program without making any important structural changes in how the program operates. Medicaid was already in near-crisis, even before this expansion, which primarily begins in 2014. States are buckling under the weight of its costs, and the networks of physicians and hospitals willing to see large numbers of Medicaid patients continue to shrink. Moreover, the distortions present in today's Medicaid matching program for federal financial support, which encourage high costs, will be made even worse as the new law temporarily increases the federal match for all states to 100 percent for the population of new program participants, beginning in 2014. The states will respond to this incentive quite predictably, by dropping any remaining efforts to control Medicaid's costs for newly eligible enrollees and by looking for ways to push even more costs off of their books and onto the federal budget while they can.

A more sustainable, market-based, and patient-centered version of health reform must avoid the core problems that stem from taxpayer support of health insurance through a defined benefits structure. Whether they arise in state Medicaid programs, the traditional Medicare program, or the tax exclusion for employer-sponsored insurance (ESI), those problems all point in the same direction. Taxpayer support for defined health benefits provides strong incentives for beneficiaries to spend more, not less (particularly on the margin) for health care services whose costs seemingly are paid largely with other people's money. As long as those defined health benefits are treated as open-ended legal entitlements, they will continue to place mounting pressure on federal and state government budgets.

The damaging consequences in health policy of defined benefits go well beyond fiscal concerns. They touch at the very nature and structure of health care decision making. Publicly financed defined health benefits invite third (insurers), fourth (employers), and fifth (government) parties into the patient-doctor relationship and increase their role. They confuse patients and medical providers as to who are the real buyers and sellers (or principals and agents) in medical matters, and where the lines are drawn between what is determined personally and what must be handled politically. They suppress cost sensitivity on the patient demand side and competition to deliver better value on the medical supply side.

Contrary to the initial promises often made by their advocates, taxpayer-financed defined health benefits eventually are prone to produce a host of inequities in practice. Particularly within the U.S. political culture, they have proved more likely to be regressive instead of progressive (or at least more random) in their pattern of distribution. When taxpayer support for defined health benefits remains open-ended and the ceiling on the latter's apparent generosity is unadjusted for a beneficiary's ability and willingness to pay, the floor of public support for special treatment for the most vulnerable beneficiaries often buckles first.

The Defined Contribution Route to Choice and Competition

A different path to health reform would rely on a defined contribution structure for taxpayer support of access to necessary health services. Defined contribution payments are made more directly and transparently to beneficiaries than the various mechanisms that launder, hide, and redirect the amount and nature of defined benefit promises through other third-party intermediaries.

Defined contributions would empower and encourage consumers and patients to make better health care choices. They would stimulate more innovative and accountable competition by health care providers. And they would encourage us all to save and invest so that we can pay more for health care when it delivers more value, but redirect our resources elsewhere when it delivers less.

How can we make this transition from defined health benefits to defined contributions?[1] An integrated approach to health care financing reform would apply the defined contribution strategy to the three main insurance-coverage platforms supported by taxpayers today: Medicare, Medicaid, and ESI. Each of these platforms needs more transparent and meaningful market-based price signals on the margin. Switching taxpayer support for them from the form of defined benefit subsidies to those of defined contributions would help make the limits of public financing more transparent, renegotiable, and more rationally allocated. After all, no one actually gets 100 cents in subsidies for each dollar of health spending (even under the current system), and many do and should receive much less.

Levels of defined contribution support from taxpayers obviously need to differ, depending primarily on the needs and nature of the population in question. For example, Medicaid beneficiaries have the lowest incomes and assets on which to draw to pay for their own health care. Medicare beneficiaries vary much more in income and wealth, but their advanced ages limit their opportunities to earn more and accumulate additional savings. Although their individual health status may vary across age and eligibility categories, both Medicaid and Medicare beneficiaries in general are likely to present more costly health-risk profiles and need more extensive health services. In contrast, many working-age beneficiaries of the current tax exclusion are likely to need less support, remain by definition "healthier" (they can go to work, after all), and should be more capable of independent decision making regarding health care purchasing choices. Moreover, other more refined adjustments in levels of tax support to beneficiaries within a given insurance category would remain necessary. They should be primarily based on such factors as relative income and health risk, but perhaps also geography.

This integrated approach to defined contribution taxpayer financing would apply several basic features, regardless of whether the coverage in question was obtained through Medicaid, Medicare, or ESI. Although defined contribution public dollars from taxpayers to support such coverage would be limited, the spending of additional private dollars to enhance or expand coverage would not be restricted. Supplemental benefits (paid for exclusively with private dollars) could vary widely, beyond a baseline definition of core coverage (and its actuarial equivalents) that would be supported in whole or in part through taxpayers' defined contributions. The better version of defined contribution health benefits would not just place initial control and choice of how to spend those taxpayer subsidies in the hands of beneficiaries; it also would provide an enhanced infrastructure of health information and connections to intermediary agents to assist them in making their choices more actionable and effective.

A Defined Contribution Approach for Medicaid Reform

Medicaid was originally established to provide health coverage for welfare recipients. Most states established automatic "categorical" eligibility for Medicaid to their residents who also were enrolled in other federal programs that legally entitled them to welfare assistance (primarily under the Aid to Families with Dependent Children program before the latter was reformed extensively in the mid-1990s). Over the years, Medicaid has moved away from that approach, with more eligibility for coverage based strictly on income tests that vary by state. But even today, Medicaid is not integrated into the insurance system for working-age Americans. It stands apart as a separate structure, with no coordination or transition between Medicaid coverage and private health insurance. This lack of coordination between the two spheres of insurance for lower-income Americans causes serious problems for Medicaid beneficiaries. When they earn more, they often lose eligibility for Medicaid, even if they face uncertain insurance prospects in the employer-based market. This continues to create strong disincentives to gain employment and move up the wage scale. Movement back and forth between Medicaid and private insurance plans can also disrupt ongoing relationships with physicians who are in private insurance networks but not part of a state's Medicaid plan.

A move to replace both traditional Medicaid assistance and the tax preference for ESI with defined contribution payments for both kinds of insurance would open up new possibilities for explicit and beneficial coordination between the Medicaid program and the coverage normally offered to working-age Americans. For example, the financial contributions from taxpayers for health insurance coverage could be restructured so that all working-age Americans and their families receive a baseline amount of assistance. It might be set as equal to their proportionate share of the value of eliminating the current exclusion of employer-paid premiums from federal income and payroll taxes. In most past formulations of this proposal, a fixed, refundable tax credit would be paid to all American households. That could be explicitly amended to include those who otherwise would also be eligible for Medicaid. Medicaid funds could then supplement this financing mechanism for those with especially low incomes who need additional support beyond that base amount (from the reallocated funds of the tax exclusion) to pay for more of their remaining premiums and cost sharing. These add-on Medicaid payments could then be phased down gradually in steps to avoid large disincentives for the beneficiaries to climb the wage and income ladder on their own.

Integration of the taxpayer-provided financial assistance side would then allow better coordination and more portable insurance for low-income families who also work. One approach might give states an incentive to develop specific insurance-selection structures that allow Medicaid beneficiaries to enroll in the same kinds of plans as workers with higher wages. To reap the benefits of moving toward a defined contribution system based on full consumer choice of competing plans offering different models for accessing services, Medicaid participants would have a greater share of their premiums subsidized by the combined tax credit and at least a substantial portion of the Medicaid payments for which they previously were eligible. But those beneficiaries still would face some additional costs if they chose to enroll in more expensive coverage options.

An early model for this approach is the insurance exchange now in use in

Utah. It is a facilitator of defined contribution payments, portable insurance, and consumer choice. If other states developed a similar model and Medicaid support were converted into a defined contribution payment as well for a state's nondisabled and nonelderly enrollees, those beneficiaries could be folded into the same insurance-selection model as many other state residents. This would give those Medicaid beneficiaries coverage they could retain even as they move up the wage ladder, thus avoiding disruptions in their care for themselves and their spouses and children, while putting pressure on the plans they choose to offer value and quality to keep them as paying customers.

Of course, states have been granted authority already, if they choose to exercise it, to use Medicaid funds to subsidize the purchase of private health insurance for eligible beneficiaries, such as coverage sponsored by their employer, through premium assistance programs. At least thirty-nine states operate some form of premium assistance through their Medicaid or Children's Health Insurance Program (CHIP). States have the option to use wraparound coverage that supplements an employer's health plan benefits and pays for some or all of its cost sharing and thereby delivers the same coverage as any other beneficiary in the states' traditional Medicaid programs.

However, enrollees in such options account for less than 1 percent of total Medicaid/CHIP enrollment and an even smaller portion of those two programs' spending.[2] Among the impediments to greater use of premium assistance are federal and state price controls that shift costs to private payers.[3] Such premium assistance also must maneuver through complex and costly administrative procedures. Lack of affordable (or any) employer-sponsored coverage for many low-income workers, on the one hand, or employers' concern that additional enrollment will increase their own health plan costs, on the other hand, further limit the potential of premium assistance.

A different approach to Medicaid reform would rely on transferring the federal government's financial share to state governments as block grants. The main political stumbling blocks facing such grant proposals involve disagreements over how those funds would be reallocated among the states (in other words, who wins and who loses), how generously they might be adjusted in the future relative to projected health care costs, and what level of current federal guarantees and minimum standards should be maintained. Giving state governments a different aggregate allotment of Medicaid funding and more discretion, by itself, does not necessarily solve the problems of lack of informed choice, insufficiently vigorous competition in benefits design, and poor incentives for improved health care delivery.

Proposals for opt out vouchers aim to encourage at least some beneficiaries to move from traditional Medicaid coverage into a choice of market-oriented private health insurance alternatives. The concept itself is attractive at the theoretical level. The nature of Medicaid coverage as a defined benefits welfare entitlement tends to focus on ensuring that its rules for eligibility and benefits remain fixed, thereby leaving only its costs as the program's primary variable. When those costs later drift upward (to meet the other two guarantees), government policymakers then are driven to try to control them through more intrusive regulation and administered prices. If financial assistance for Medicaid coverage instead were delivered to beneficiaries as a defined contribution, then taxpayer costs and program eligibility rules would be held relatively more constant, but the nature, level, and quality of Medicaid's health benefits would become more variable. Such an approach would reward insurers, health care providers and state policymakers for raising the quality of health care, the value of health benefits, and the satisfaction of patients instead of just struggling to keep the apparent costs of the program lower.[4]

In practice, converting this idea into workable and sustainable policy reform at the state level has been uphill thus far, in large part because Medicaid reform has stood in isolation from the employer market from which many Medicaid recipients bounce back and forth while periodically receiving Medicaid. In recent years, various state-level proposals for Medicaid vouchers have failed either to gain legislative approval or to build enough momentum to demonstrate clear evidence of success. Even a particularly promising blueprint for new private insurance options in Florida's Medicaid program has not yet reached critical mass and convinced skeptics.[5]

Hence, future efforts to develop a defined contribution alternative to

Medicaid's defined benefit entitlement will need to proceed with a clear integration plan with the employer market, so that choices made by Medicaid recipients can be retained even as they move out of Medicaid financing into other private coverage financed in part with tax credits. They should target initially that portion of the Medicaid beneficiary population that is below age sixty-five, nondisabled, and looking for a qualitative upgrade from coverage that promises seemingly generous benefits but pays providers too little to deliver them.

New defined contribution alternatives for insurance must be allowed to include a different mix of benefits, cost sharing, and medical-care management than traditional Medicaid. The current political climate makes the discretionary approval of Medicaid waivers for such experiments less likely and a broader legislative overhaul of the program's financing more necessary. States pursuing more market-based, consumer-choice reforms also should acknowledge that they may have to decide on a different mix of policies that include covering fewer people, leaving more details of health spending decisions to beneficiaries ready and eager to make them, paying participating health care providers for the full costs of care, and measuring its delivered quality more accurately.

Delinking levels of state spending from federal spending on this portion of Medicaid would be equally important. The primary policy options include the politically treacherous overhaul of the FMAP rules that reward richer states at the expense of poorer ones and encourage additional state Medicaid spending on the margin to maximize matching federal dollars.[6] Rearranging the federal share of Medicaid funding into block grants to states, with future annual updates indexed somewhat below current Medicaid spending projections, traditionally provides a formulaic short cut. However, a more aggressive approach would limit federal assistance to fully funding just the upper layers of catastrophic acute care for the below-sixty-five, nondisabled portion of Medicaid, while states become responsible for financing as much of the coverage and cost sharing below those levels as they decide to handle. The latter type of reform would place much greater reliance on defined contribution assistance (through refundable tax credits) to Medicaid beneficiaries and direct contracting by state programs with competing private insurance plans.

Since its enactment in the 1960s, Medicaid has mainly been considered a health insurance program for nonworking welfare recipients and others who cannot access employer-sponsored coverage. Moving from a defined benefit to defined contribution structure allows a wholesale rethinking of the existing paradigm. With defined contributions, Medicaid could be integrated into the same private insurance marketplace populated with workers and their families, and thus allow more seamless transitions as Medicaid families move into higher-paying jobs.

Nearer-Term Options: Capped Entitlements & Expanded Managed Care

There are near-term limits to the likelihood of implementing a defined contribution approach on a broad basis and its application to the costliest and most medically complex Medicaid beneficiaries – the aged, blind, and disabled (many of whom are dually eligible for Medicare coverage) – is even more problematic. Developing more immediate, practical reforms for chronic problems in ongoing Medicaid coverage is also needed.[7]

In particular, the program's many rules at the federal level, and the thousands of pages of regulations defining just what they mean, repeatedly hamstring state flexibility, innovation, and cost containment efforts. The process for states to seek a waiver from the federal government is often lengthy and time consuming. As a result, too many important elements of the current system remain trapped in a one-size-fits-all approach with little meaningful competition for services. For example, one federal rule provides that medical assistance must be made available to those who qualify for Medicaid as categorically needy and categorically related eligible persons in the same "amount, duration, or scope…,"[8] thus limiting states' ability to create targeted benefits packages for specific populations or put reasonable limits on benefits for certain populations.[9] Another federal Medicaid rule provides that similarly situated individuals must receive comparable services. Some courts have held that this comparability provision is violated whenever there is a disparity of treatment within categorically-needy beneficiary populations, even when those individuals suffer from different kinds and degrees of disabilities.[10]

The federal government also restricts state efforts to limit Medicaid beneficiaries' right to choose a health care provider, including the location of the services, even when more narrow alternatives might be more cost effective and improve the quality of care delivered. Another federal rule provides that a Medicaid beneficiary (not the state that is paying for a large portion of the covered benefits) is free to choose any "institution, agency, community pharmacy, or person, qualified to perform the service of services required….who undertakes to provide such services…"[11] States that consider implementing a broader managed-care approach to most of their programs first must be granted federal waivers from this unrestricted choice of provider rule – a process which exhausts precious time and resources and delays necessary reforms.

The most recent urgent concern for states already struggling to maneuver through difficult budgetary environments involves the maintenance of effort (MOE) provision imposed on them in the PPACA. MOE instructs states that they cannot reduce or restrict eligibility to Medicaid programs below the level that was in place at the time the law was enacted on March 23, 2010. PPACA will increase states' Medicaid costs in other ways, particularly when it encourages higher numbers of previously-eligible people to enroll in the Medicaid program. One congressional report, "Medicaid Expansion in the New Health Law: Costs to the States," recently issued jointly by the Senate Finance Committee, Minority and the House Energy and Commerce Committee, Majority estimated that PPACA will cost state taxpayers at least $118.04 billion through 2023 – more than double the Congressional Budget Office's recent estimate of $60 billion through 2021.[12]

PPACA also expands Medicaid eligibility "out posting" (adding new venues to sign up for Medicaid), creates new health insurance exchanges beginning on January 1, 2014, and adds federal penalties for those who are uninsured on or after that date. As a result, millions of the currently uninsured who are already Medicaid-eligible are expected to find their way onto state Medicaid caseloads. However, these individuals will not receive the enhanced federal match rate available to the "newly-eligible" expansion population expected to receive

Medicaid coverage beginning in 2014 under the PPACA. They will instead be financed under traditional FMAP guidelines, and thus require a more substantial contribution from state government budgets.

Working Models of State-Based Medicaid Innovation

A few states have explored more creative alternatives to work around the federal barriers to better Medicaid practices. The State of Rhode Island received a Global Medicaid waiver in 2009 to establish a new state-federal compact. In exchange for much more flexibility to run its state Medicaid program, Rhode Island agreed to provide the federal government with greater fiscal certainty. Under the waiver, Rhode Island promised to operate its Medicaid program under an aggregate budget cap of $12.075 billion (combined federal and state spending) over a five-year period. This aggregate amount was determined by looking at Rhode Island's historic total Medicaid spending trend rate for the years 2002 through 2006, plus the federal government's actuary report for 2008 — which projected total Medicaid spending for the next 10 years.[13] A $12.075 billion five-year aggregate total for Medicaid spending was calculated by using 2006 as the base year and trending forward at a rate of 7.9% per year. The first-of-its-kind Rhode Island agreement capped the federal government's obligations for an entitlement at a fixed level. If the state program spends more than this average trend rate and total spending exceeds the cap, Rhode Island is responsible for 100% of those additional costs.

The underlying rationale for capping total Medicaid spending is that open-ended federal matching of funds for Medicaid spending by states has encouraged the latter to expand the size, scope, and cost of their Medicaid programs to unsustainable levels. On the other hand, capping the total federal funding allotment available to a state would encourage it to concentrate more on improving the program's performance and less on how to leverage additional federal dollars.

The Rhode Island waiver is not a block grant.[14] It preserves the FMAP formula for determining the relative federal share of the total level of the state

Medicaid program's spending, but it caps that aggregate spending through 2013. Within these federal funding limits, the state was given greater freedom to design and redesign its program. Rhode Island could organize and deliver services in a more targeted and cost-effective manner, across populations and acute and long-term care settings, to address the complex and inter-related needs of beneficiaries throughout their life-cycle. The state also could leverage its purchasing power to create new provider markets or drive change in existing ones through competition. It gained the freedom to implement strategies already successful in the commercial health insurance market that encourage and reward beneficiaries who take responsibility for their own health and wellness.

Moreover, the state was given a great degree of flexibility in administering its own Medicaid program. Prior to the waiver, the state would have to seek federal approval for any small or minor change in state plan services, and then wait months and perhaps years for any approval of an innovative change that could lead to real meaningful savings and improve quality of care. The waiver established a new review process in which the level of federal scrutiny was more commensurate with the scope of change within the state's Medicaid program.

The waiver also eases reporting requirements for Medicaid services, thus reducing bureaucratic delays and red tape that add substantial costs, put additional demands on state workforce, and create a drag on agency efficiency. Under the waiver, Rhode Island now submits quarterly reports to CMS for just one seamless waiver. Previously, the state had to submit individual reports for every one of its waiver services within five different state agencies.

The early results are promising. In the first eighteen months under the global waiver, estimated savings are $100 million, and the rate of growth in total Medicaid spending has been reduced by more than half, from 7.94% to 3%. If the state's Medicaid spending continues on the same path for the next three years, it will amount to a few billion dollars less than the cap agreed to for the five-year demonstration.

Moreover, Rhode Island has used this new administrative flexibility to make a number of important changes in the way it administers its Medicaid program. For example, Rhode Island has successfully implemented many related Medicaid reforms, such as rebalancing long-term care, keeping more seniors in community settings rather than expensive nursing homes, incentivizing higher quality care, designing wellness programs to prevent the need for more expensive care, purchasing reforms to increase competition, and giving beneficiaries more direct control over health care spending.

A different example of recent innovation in Medicaid policy at the state level involves Florida's section 1115 Medicaid Reform Waiver. This comprehensive demonstration was designed to improve the value of the state's Medicaid delivery system by coupling the increased use of managed care principles with innovative approaches like customized benefit packages, opt-out provisions, and health-related incentives or enhanced benefits for beneficiaries. The Florida waiver offers participating Medicaid beneficiaries choices in health plan benefit packages that are tailored to provide services that better suit their needs. The waiver authorizes the state to allow private health plans that agree to a per-member per-month capitated amount to create more innovative, customized benefit package by varying certain services for non-pregnant adults, cost-sharing, and the scope of additional services provided. The state also added an effective component of personal responsibility to the waiver, called the Enhanced Benefits Account Program (EBAP). EBAP promotes and rewards beneficiaries for participating in healthy behaviors, such as well-baby check-ups and immunizations, age-appropriate health screenings, and participation in disease management programs.

In July 2009-July 2010, the waiver program operated in five counties and had 350,000 enrollees. During that fiscal year, average monthly costs to the state and federal governments among elderly and low-income children were 28 percent lower for waiver enrollees than for non-waiver enrollees, yielding savings of $2.5 billion in 2010.

Moreover, access to providers has also improved under the plan. In March 2009, 99% of providers surveyed had contracts with the Medicaid Reform health plans.[15] As a result of wellness incentives, reform counties outperformed non-reform counties on 20 out of 27 quality measures (non-HEDIS) of preventive care.[16] As of 2010, beneficiaries have earned $30.4 million in credits for health promotion activities.[17] Finally, enrollees in reform counties were more satisfied than those in control counties.[18]

Although these examples of state innovation within the limits of the current Medicaid system show promise,[19] truly meaningful and cost-effective Medicaid reform must begin with substantial changes to the financing of Medicaid at the federal level. The open-ended federal reimbursement of at least half, and often more, of state Medicaid program expenditures creates strong incentives for states to spend carelessly. Each state's Medicaid program ends up larger than it would be if its own taxpayers had to pay the entire cost. This upward long-term bias toward greater state Medicaid spending discourages more timely responsible reforms and pushes state programs beyond their sustainable limits.

Putting Medicaid on a more fixed budget would provide budgetary certainty at both levels of government. It would discourage states from leveraging additional federal taxpayer money through the FMAP reimbursement formula and impose more discipline on state programs. By knowing the likely amount of federal assistance to expect in future years, state Medicaid programs could be managed more carefully for the long haul. Either a broad block grant of federal funds to a state or a capped allotment to federal funds through the current FMAP formula provides states with upfront funding over a predetermined period of time. Such initially "fixed" funding should come with incentives – if the state spends below the grant it can use the savings for other areas of state needs just like in the Temporary Assistance to Needy Families program. Congress can also provide bonus payments for each state if it achieves appropriate benchmarks.

The federal government should allow states to determine their own eligibility categories and income threshold levels for Medicaid; establish rates and service delivery options; design benefit packages that best meet the demographic, public health, and cultural needs of each state or region (whether this involves adding, deleting or modifying benefits); and use cost-sharing as a way to promote individual responsibility for personal health and wellness.

In order to properly coordinate the care for the dual eligible beneficiaries and provide many of them with more preventive primary care and other cost effective services, Medicare and Medicaid must work together. The federal government must allow states the option to enroll all their dual eligibles in mandatory managed care plans and share in savings that occur across both programs. This change would energize states to pursue new care coordination initiatives, tailored to the needs of older, low-income beneficiaries.

However, managed care for an increased share of Medicaid beneficiaries is no panacea. Its effects on costs and quality depend on how well it is executed in practice, as well as the setting in which it occurs. Medicaid program contracts with managed care providers in theory offer a mechanism to hold participating health plans or providers more accountable for the health outcomes and patient experience of Medicaid enrollees through various performance standards. A recent 50-state survey of Medicaid managed care programs by the Kaiser Commission on Medicaid and the Uninsured indicates that states are increasingly mandating managed care for previously exempt or excluded Medicaid beneficiaries and that such programs already cover about two-thirds of all Medicaid beneficiaries.[20] Broader efforts to focus managed care on dual eligibles are expanding or getting underway. These projected expansions are driven both by severe state budget pressures and interest in improving access to and quality of care for Medicaid beneficiaries.

A cautionary note comes from a new study by Duggan and Hayford, which examined detailed data on state Medicaid expenditures from 1991 to 2003.[21] They found that shifting Medicaid recipients from traditional fee-for-service benefits programs into Medicaid managed care ones did not reduce Medicaid spending in the typical state. Effects of the shift varied significantly across states as a function of the relative generosity of the state's baseline Medicaid provider reimbursement rates. In states where Medicaid provider reimbursement is very low relative to commercial reimbursement rates, managed care contracting seemed to *increase* Medicaid spending, and vice versa. The likely explanation is that most managed care programs achieve their savings primarily through obtaining lower prices rather than producing reduced quantities of health care services. Duggan and Hayford acknowledge that aged and disabled Medicaid recipients may differ in many respects from most of the Medicaid recipients previously affected by managed care mandates. Yet, given that current and future Medicaid reimbursement rates appear to be moving downward amidst severe budgetary pressures and few other cost-reducing options are available for state policy makers, their overall analysis does not bode well for the future effects of Medicaid managed care.

A recent set of additional state-based Medicaid reform recommendation by the Republican Governors Public Policy Committee include providing states with enhanced options to reward individuals who participate in health promotion or disease prevention activities, and to offer "value-added" or additional services for individuals choosing a lower-cost plan. Its health care task force also called for a necessary re-examination of obsolete federal Medicaid rules for "mandatory" versus "optional" benefits.[22]

Each state Medicaid program should be accountable for measured improvement in health care quality – whether through better health outcomes or performance metrics – rather than just how closely it complies with rules and regulation that often have little if any real impact on the lives of beneficiaries and fail to promote efficiency and cost containment. In a block grant or capped allotment approach to Medicaid reform, the primary role of the federal government should be to ensure that there is true accountability and responsibility on the part of states given greater freedom in spending federal dollars. The federal government should offer every state the opportunity to enter into a simplified compact that sets outcome measures and benchmarks and requires a participating state to report periodically (perhaps quarterly) on its performance in achieving them. Federal oversight should only be triggered when there is a significant deviation in the reported versus projected performance. The number of measures should be limited to ten for each of the three dimensions of healthcare: cost, quality, and access. This will simplify or eliminate the state plan approval process, allowing states to concentrate more on what matters most – better health outcomes, better value, and lower costs.

Part 2

One Experiment: Massachusetts

5

Competing Visions for Massachusetts: Health Reform

Jennifer Heldt Powell

Part 1: Deriving the Massachusetts Health Reform

On the morning of April 12, 2006, the stage was set for a grand, unified drive to expand health care coverage and lower costs in Massachusetts. Leaders from both parties would stand side by side with health care providers, insurers, businesses, and unions to endorse a new law that would require health insurance for everyone in the Commonwealth.

Historic Faneuil Hall was packed with everyone who was anyone in the health care world, ranging from hospital presidents to insurance CEOs to activists. Although many held firm to their skepticism, there was a palpable sense of hope that this legislation would fundamentally change the system for the better.

Just behind the stage, however, this triumphant, unified image was marred by the angry looks and words of top lawmakers as they read Governor Mitt Romney's press release for the event. He planned to veto several key provisions, including a $295 annual per person penalty on businesses that failed to provide health insurance for their employees. He had also announced his intentions to veto these provisions in a *Wall Street Journal* opinion piece that day.

The Great Experiment

The ceremony went on as planned, with jocular speeches and other appropriate pleasantries, but in the hours that followed, lawmakers were vociferous about how blindsided and betrayed they felt.

Their protestations came despite feeling fairly certain that the vetoes would be overridden and the legislation would stand as written. Romney did not expect the vetoes to stand, but he was publicly distancing himself from provisions in the law that he felt were ineffective and unnecessary without negating the pieces he felt were crucial.

The governor's vetoes reflected the level of contention in the debate over the months leading up to the historic bill signing. More significantly, Governor Romney's vetoes foreshadowed the challenges ahead. The new law was mostly a framework, with key issues yet to be decided. The final decisions about those issues would ultimately dictate the success or failure of the plan.

To understand the complexities of the final compromise and how it ultimately unfolded in the five years since it became law, it is important to understand the context in which it was created.

Primed for Health Care Reform

With its top-notch hospitals and leading research facilities, Massachusetts is a world leader in health care, but its health care carries a price. Between 1991 and 2004, per capita health care expenditures in the Bay State increased 106 percent, to $6,683 from $3,249. The national increase during that time was 100 percent, to $5,283 from $2,654.[1]

Not surprisingly, the issue has been a recurring topic in Massachusetts political circles. Along with debates about how to control cost, access has also been a recurrent concern. There has long been an undercurrent of support for universal health care in one form or another, although this drive was often overshadowed by other pressing issues.

The Commonwealth moved toward universal coverage in the late 1980s when Michael Dukakis was governor. Under his leadership, and after months of contentious negotiations, the legislature adopted a "pay or play" mandate.

Companies with more than six employees would have faced a surcharge of $1,680 per worker if they failed to provide coverage. The plan was supposed to be phased in over several years, but the political and economic climate changed before it was fully implemented, and support for the mandate faded.

The law was repealed without ever being fully implemented in the 1990s under Governor William Weld, who made other changes to the health care system, including price deregulation and a halt to state hospital rate setting. Additionally, the Weld administration slowed Medicaid cost growth through cuts in provider payments, a heavier reliance on managed care, and reduced welfare caseloads.[2]

A New Governor, a New Perspective

The forces that had lobbied for the universal coverage effort under Dukakis were still at work when Romney took office in January 2003. Additionally, early in his administration, Romney himself became interested in structural health care reforms. The issue was pushed off, however, as the administration dealt with more urgent matters such as the state's $3 billion deficit and the struggling economy.

Health care moved toward center stage in 2004 as the legislature gave preliminary approval to a sweeping constitutional amendment that would guarantee health insurance for all residents. This measure was vague, calling for laws to ensure that no one would lack "comprehensive, affordable and equitably financed" health insurance; however, it offered no specifics on how to accomplish this goal. The measure was also widely considered a long shot: as a constitutional amendment, it had to be endorsed by voters and needed further approval from lawmakers before it could even be put on the ballot.

Still, this measure began to define the parameters of the debate. Moving forward, lawmakers focused primarily on expanding health insurance coverage and using the existing, largely employer-based health insurance marketplace differently. There were fringe discussions about a single payer system, though this never became a mainstream alternative.

The Great Experiment

While lawmakers talked publicly about health care reform options, Romney worked behind the scenes developing his own vision. Initially, his objective was to find a way to redirect the money the State was spending on care for low income residents without insurance; he wanted to convert the money to subsidies that would enable the uninsured to afford health insurance. As he worked on his approach, one of his top officials crafted a white paper concluding that it was possible to cover everyone in the state. The report, however, also suggested that it would take additional revenue and suggested a fee on employers of $150 a month for every full-time employee who did not have health insurance.

Even in that early stage of the debate, Romney adamantly rejected the concept of an employer mandate. He continued working on a plan that would instead be centered on personal responsibility.

A Health Care Crisis Looms

Throughout this period, health care reform was becoming increasingly critical to the State's finances. The Commonwealth's 2004 household insurance survey estimated that 460,000 people, roughly 8 percent of the population in Massachusetts, were without health insurance, up by 42,000 from two years prior. The Urban Institute estimated that the cost of caring for those without insurance topped $1 billion.[3]

Massachusetts was soon to face pressure from the Federal government to change the way it paid to care for those without insurance and those who were covered by MassHealth, the Commonwealth's Medicaid plan. Massachusetts had been operating under a waiver from the US Department of Health and Human Services that allowed flexibility in how Medicaid funds were spent. The waiver was set to expire on July 1, 2005, and without a new one, the state would lose $385 million in Federal Medicaid funding.

The growing number of uninsured was putting pressure on the Commonwealth's uncompensated care pool. This was a fund created in the mid-1980s to reimburse hospitals and community health centers that provide "free care" to low income, uninsured residents. It was supported by payments from hospitals and insurers, along with State and Federal contributions. In the fiscal year that ended in 2004, the pool provided care for 450,000 individuals at a cost of $720 million.[4] Hospitals that paid more into the pool than they received from it said that the rising costs were straining their budgets. Those that provided the most uncompensated care, primarily large urban hospitals, said the pool did not cover their costs. Hospital administrators clamored for change.

By October 2004, impatient lawmakers started to push the issue with a proposal that did not have to go to the ballot. Democratic leaders of the House and Senate Health Care Committees announced that they were working on a plan that would increase access to MassHealth and expand the Insurance Partnership, a program for small businesses. Furthermore, they said they were considering a "pay or play" plan requiring businesses to provide insurance benefits or pay into a state program.

A month later, Senate President Robert E. Travaglini outlined his ideas to cover at least half of those without insurance by the end of 2006. This would be done in part by allowing cheaper, less-comprehensive health insurance plans to enter the Massachusetts marketplace. Additionally, Medicaid payments to providers would be increased. The reasoning was based on the premise that providers were typically reimbursed at 80 percent of their costs, and that they passed those losses on to insurers. In theory, more money coming from the government would allow providers to charge everyone else less.

The Senate plan did not include an employer mandate. However, it would have charged employers that did not provide coverage if their workers received care through the Uncompensated Care Pool.

A short time later, Romney publicly sketched out the plan he had been working on. Dubbed "Commonwealth Care," it would cover virtually everyone in the state. It did not include a "pay or play" component, relying instead on a "carrot and stick" approach, as Romney explained in a *Boston Globe* opinion piece when the plan was released.[5]

"It will not require new taxes," he wrote. "What it will do is restrain the growth in healthcare costs and change how we provide healthcare for those who receive it at taxpayers' expense. And, it can lead to every citizen in Massachusetts having health care."

Insurers would be allowed to develop policies without strict state mandates, which would make insurance more affordable, he said. There would be a greater effort to enroll into Medicaid those who were eligible but who had not joined: people who were receiving care through the Uncompensated Care Pool. At the same time, Governor Romney called for increased fraud detection and penalties, and the inclusion of the income of parents not living at home to determine whether families were eligible.

The Uncompensated Care Pool would be replaced with the Health Safety Net program, which would provide a managed care approach and require those who used it to pay according to their means. A new state entity, the "Commonwealth Care Exchange," would oversee the new health plan offerings.

In the spring, activists weighed in with yet another plan, which they intended to put on the 2006 ballot. The proposal made by Affordable Care Today would have increased the cigarette tax to raise revenue, and it would have required all but very small employers to provide health insurance to workers.

Affordable Care Today launched the ballot initiative with a carefully calculated plan. Its intention was to push the legislature into action. If the legislature failed to act within a few months, the ballot measure would keep the issue alive with a vote in the fall. This was a formidable interest group, given its size and public voice. The coalition included Health Care for All, which was led by former state lawmaker John McDonough, who had co-authored a major state health care expansion in 1996. Additionally, there were more than 150 progressive religious groups, labor unions, social service organizations and other community organizations. These were vocal, politically savvy advocates who organized rallies and knew how to raise attention to an issue. They needed 40,000 signatures to get on the ballot, which they ultimately collected.

Ideas Turn Into Concrete Proposals

In April 2005, Travaglini turned his outline into legislation. Governor Romney followed within a week, introducing two health care reform bills to the

House. The first plan to be voted on, however, came from the House leadership on October 31. This proposal by House Speaker Salvatore DiMasi included pieces of both Travaglini and Romney's plans, along with some significant differences.

DiMasi's plan would have increased the number of people covered by MassHealth and raised the reimbursement rate to MassHealth providers, as Travaglini proposed. DiMasi also wanted to merge the non-group and small group health insurance markets (first proposed by Romney). The most controversial piece of the plan called for a payroll tax of 5 percent on companies with between 11 and 100 employees and 7 percent on companies with more than 100 workers. Health care coverage provided by companies would have been deductible against the levy.

The House bill passed 131 to 22 on November 3, 2005. The plan was not acceptable to the Senate. Travaglini stripped the bill and replaced it with new language. However, his bill, as with the House plan, did include an expansion of Medicaid to cover children in households earning up to 300 percent of the federal poverty level (FPL), or $48,270 for a family of three. The standard at the time was 200 percent of poverty or $32,180 for a family of three. That move would have brought an estimated 37,000 children into the state program at a cost of $105 million.

This plan passed the Senate unanimously; the House refused to accept this plan. On November 14, the chamber voted not to concur with the Senate. Two days later, conferees from both chambers were appointed to work out a compromise, but they did not start meeting in earnest until January.

As lawmakers began hammering out an agreement, business leaders launched a public campaign in December opposing an employer mandate.[6]

The $200,000 effort included print ads and a 60-second radio spot warning that the law was bad for job growth and the economy.

Helping to keep the debate alive, the influential US Senator Edward M. Kennedy got involved, urging everyone involved to reach a compromise. Romney also continued to reach out to lawmakers, even going so far as making unannounced visits to their homes.

Still, as the impasse dragged on into the end of February, Travaglini gave up on broad reform. Instead, the Senate took up a scaled-back version in hopes of doing at least enough to save the $385 million in Federal money.

One of the biggest disagreements was over an assessment on employers that did not provide health insurance. DiMasi insisted on it, but Romney and Travaglini opposed the idea.

The Senate's newer plan was intended to cover just half the uninsured with new, subsidized insurance plans. It included a mandate that would kick in if the State could not reduce the number of uninsured. Travaglini described it as a placeholder to satisfy the Federal government.

House leader DiMasi refused to accept the scaled-back version, saying he felt the State would miss an opportunity for sweeping reforms. He also implied that there was room for a compromise. In response, Travaglini took a step toward an agreement by indicating that the Senate might be willing to approve an assessment on businesses that did not provide health insurance. It was not a payroll tax, but it was enough to get the conversation moving.

Around this time, several of the State's top business leaders, including some with heavy ties to the health care industry, got closely involved in helping to broker an agreement.[7] They made plans in closed-door meetings with legislative leaders. The business leaders agreed to support a fee on businesses that did not provide health insurance. This cleared the way for the rest of the compromise. Additionally, MassHealth would be slightly expanded, and there would be a new subsidized health plan for low income residents. The individual and non-group markets would be merged.

With this loose agreement in place, the details were quickly finalized so that the legislature could vote on it in time to save the Federal money. The new law was in many ways more of a framework than a detailed plan. There were outlines of what needed to be done, with deadlines, but many of the specifics of the plan's implementation were left to a quasi-public entity, the Massachusetts Commonwealth Health Insurance Connector Authority, created by the law and overseen by an appointed board of directors.

As Romney's decision to veto the $295 assessment on businesses that failed to provide health insurance and other provisions of the bill indicated, simmering disagreements remained over some of the specific provisions of the reforms.[8] Those disagreements, which had shaped the debate all along, would also shape implementation once the Connector went to work.

The bill's lack of specifics was inevitable, given the time pressure Romney and the lawmakers faced, but it prolonged the debate and created room for reforms that strayed from the expectations of those originally involved in crafting the plan.

Regardless of the direction the reforms would finally take, sweeping changes were in motion. The law contained specific and tight deadlines to advance changes. There was less of a chance that it would be delayed or derailed as had the Dukakis plan.

As he signed the bill, Romney went through with vetoing the measures he did not support. Within weeks the legislature overrode those vetoes. The votes were overwhelming but not unanimous, falling mostly along party lines.

Once the bill was signed, advocates who had been pushing for the ballot measure withdrew their proposals in a show of support for the new law. Far from being done with their work, however, they shifted their efforts to exerting influence over how the law would be implemented.

The lawmakers who were most influential in the negotiations were planning to stay in office and expected to continue pushing their agenda. Since Romney was not planning to run for reelection, his side of the discussion was at the greatest risk of being drowned out by other voices. Romney's successor, Democrat Deval Patrick, won the 2006 election and thus had a strong influence over the enactment of the reforms. While from early on his administration he maintained a commitment to making reform a success, his expectations and priorities were different than Romney's. Some measures envisioned by Romney, such as a vast open market with a wide range of insurance options including low cost plans without mandated benefits, were never realized.

A New Law, a New Direction

As a blueprint, the law set the foundation for reform. Its key components included a requirement that individuals who could afford to buy health insurance do so or face a fine. Their health insurance plans had to meet standards known as "Minimum Creditable Coverage" (MCC).

The reform also created a new state entity known as the Commonwealth Connector. This entity is governed by an unelected, appointed board of 10 people appointed by the administration, the attorney general and state officials. The Connector was given the responsibility to set regulations regarding reform and to administer new programs.

In addition, MassHealth (Medicaid) was expanded to cover children in households with incomes up to 300 percent of the federal poverty level (FPL). The reform also created a new subsidized insurance program, Commonwealth Care, for low income residents with incomes up to 300 percent of FPL who lacked access to other insurance options.

The law aimed to partially deregulate the individual market and merge the individual and small group markets. In addition to being able to buy the same health insurance products on the open market, these two groups would have the option to pool together in the Connector within a new program called Commonwealth Choice.

Employers with 11 or more full-time-equivalent employees would be assessed up to $295 per employee per year if employers were found not to be making a "fair and reasonable" contribution to the health insurance of their employees. Moreover, a "free rider" surcharge would be assessed on businesses with employees who made excessive use of the free care pool if their employers did not offer insurance.

The law also replaced the Uncompensated Care Pool with a new program called the Health Care Safety Net to cover the cost of care provided to low income individuals without insurance. Significant amounts of money were transferred out of the Uncompensated Care Pool to pay for subsidies in the Commonwealth Care program.

Finally, six new councils or commissions were created to oversee and study issues ranging from health care quality to disparities in health care.

There were, however, fundamentally significant questions about how certain measures would be carried out. For example, what would be the subsidized Commonwealth Care parameters for qualifying income levels? How much would participants have to contribute, and what benefits would they have?

What would be the standards for "Minimum Creditable Coverage" and "affordability" for purposes of determining compliance with the individual mandate? How would the individual and small group markets be merged and what options would they have? What options would be available through Commonwealth Choice? What was a "fair and reasonable" contribution for businesses?

Romney's last Secretary of Health and Human Services, Timothy Murphy, aptly explained what was coming in one of the first reports to the Connector Board:

> "Of course the Act is just hopeful words. Only through effective implementation will these words bring about the positive changes envisioned by those that shaped its passage. The path to full implementation will be difficult and will challenge all stakeholders in the health care industry."[9]

A closer look at how each section of the law has been developed over the last five years gives a clearer picture of how each was initially implemented and changed over time due to variances such as underlying ideologies as well as budgetary concerns.

Part 2: Early Implementation

The Commonwealth Connector

> "The goal of the board is to facilitate the purchase of health care insurance products through the connector at an affordable price by eligible individuals, groups & commonwealth care health insurance plan

enrollees."[10]

The Commonwealth Health Insurance Connector Authority began work in June 2006, rapidly putting into place the infrastructure necessary to create the new programs called for under the law. The first program established was Commonwealth Care, which would provide subsidized health insurance to adult residents with household incomes below 300 percent of FPL.

Following that, the Connector created an exchange through which individuals and small businesses could buy unsubsidized commercial health insurance. The exchange's intention was to provide non-traditional workers, such as part-time and seasonal workers, contractors, sole proprietors, and those with multiple jobs with the ability to purchase affordable, portable health insurance. It was also expected that the Connector would enable small businesses to offer a choice of affordable products to their employees, allowing the employees to purchase health insurance on a pre-tax basis.

The Connector was launched with a one-time appropriation of $25 million from the state's general fund. It was expected to be self-sustaining through a surcharge applied to all participating health plans. The Connector is governed by a 10-member board of directors. Although it is not considered to be a political entity, it is inevitably influenced by the ideology of those who appoint the members. This is especially relevant since the Connector was given regulatory authority and powers.

The membership includes three gubernatorial appointees; three appointees of the attorney general; 4 ex-officio members including the state's Medicaid director; the commissioner of the Division of Insurance; the director of the Group Insurance Commission (Massachusetts' insurer for state employees); and the secretary of Administration and Finance, who serves as chairman. The law originally called for an 11-member board, but only identified 10 appointments. A broker representative joined the board in July 2011. Although it is an independent public authority, it is subject to the state's open meeting law.

The Work Begins

The Romney administration chose Jon Kingsdale, a former executive from Tufts Health Plan, one of the Bay State's largest health plans, as the Connector's first executive director. Kingsdale, who remained in the position through 2010, guided the board through the many difficult decisions it faced. The first board meeting took place on June 7, 2006. It was clear that the board was under significant public scrutiny; roughly 300 people showed up for the meeting.

In some respects, it appeared to be a diverse board, at least initially. In addition to the administration officials, members included Celia Wcislo, an organizer of the Service Employees International Union, who had been a vocal supporter of the 2006 ballot initiative; Rick Lord, president of Associated Industries of Massachusetts, which had opposed the employer mandate; Jonathan Gruber, a Massachusetts Institute of Technology economist; and Charles Joffe-Halpern, the head of a nonprofit that helped people get insurance.

Much of the board's deliberation took place privately, in advance of public board meetings, and compromises were worked out by Kingsdale and Connector staff before the board took final votes. Consequently, even votes on major contentious issues were almost always unanimous.

These compromises significantly impacted the direction of the reform's implementation. The language of the reform had been written so broadly that intent could be interpreted differently based on individual board members' viewpoints. What one considered affordable, another saw as prohibitively expensive. This meant that the board was still within its mandate when it took a significantly different direction than was intended by some involved in the original compromise.

During the early stages of implementation, the board was heavily influenced by the appointees of Governor Romney and his cabinet members, who served as voting ex-officio members. Shortly after the work began, however, they were replaced by the appointees serving under Governor Deval Patrick, who had a different vision of how the reform law should be implemented. Aside from ex-officio Administration officials, the turnover on the board has been slow. Until

January 2011, four of the six appointed members had been with the board since the passage of the law.

The Connector has become a large operation with more than 45 employees managing various components of reform.

The agency developed and maintains a website, www.mahealthconnector.org, which provides separate portals for individuals, employers, employees, young adults, and brokers. On the website, individuals and small businesses are able to shop for and compare various plans. The website provides information about the individual mandate and how to apply for an exemption.

Personal Responsibility in the Law

One of the key components of the Bay State's health care reform law is the individual mandate. It was based on two assumptions: that people need to take responsibility for themselves, and that without the individual mandate, Massachusetts would not reach the goal of near-universal coverage. This point was carried throughout many of the proposals that led up to reform.

Romney explained his thinking on the issue in the opinion piece that appeared in the *Wall Street Journal* on the day he signed the bill into law: "Some of my libertarian friends balk at what looks like an individual mandate. But remember, someone has to pay for the health care that must, by law, be provided. Either the individual pays or the taxpayers pay. A free ride on government is not libertarian."[11]

With passage of the law, Massachusetts became the first state in the nation to require that residents carry health insurance. Beginning on July 1, 2007, the law required that everyone over age 18 carry a minimum level of health insurance, with an allowed lapse in coverage of no more than 63 days. In the first year, those who did not do so faced the loss of their state personal tax exemption, which was $219 for an individual. Exceptions included those claiming an exemption for religious reasons, and those who had a certificate from the Connector indicating that no health insurance offered through the Connector had been deemed affordable for that individual. In subsequent years, the penalty became equal to one-half of the premium of the least costly available insurance plan that met the state's standard.

The Individual Mandate in Practice

The simplicity of the individual mandate and language in the law hid the complexity of implementing it. For starters, there was the immense technical challenge of tracking who had insurance, who was exempt, and who was subject to penalties. This new tracking system was set up through the existing state income tax collection process, administered by the Department of Revenue (DOR). Under this system, individuals indicate on their personal income tax returns whether they have insurance or an exemption. If they have insurance, they must submit proof that the insurance meets the state's minimum standards. Any penalties collected from those without insurance are used to pay for the Commonwealth Care program.

Early technical challenges emerged because insurers had moved away from the use of social security numbers as unique client identifiers, yet the state DOR ran all of its systems based on social security numbers. The Commonwealth had to determine exactly what information was required, how to report it safely, and with what frequency. To ensure appropriate input, the Department of Insurance held several industry meetings with the Executive Office of Health and Human Services and the DOR to identify the issues and find solutions.

The law called for creating a database of all insured individuals by January 1, 2008, to be managed by the Health Access Bureau at the Division of Insurance. The DOR was responsible for assessing penalties beginning in 2008 and needed an accurate and reliable system. Administering the individual mandate also required insurance companies to make significant operational changes. For example, insurers now are required to provide verification of minimum creditable coverage to each person they cover.

The Minimum Bar for Coverage

Even more significant than these technicalities, however, was the outstanding question of what would qualify as adequate health insurance under the vague "Minimum Creditable Coverage" standard that the law established. This was one of the most controversial decisions made by the Connector board. There were some, including Romney, who focused more on affordability. They envisioned health insurance options that included the basics but allowed higher co-payments or deductibles to keep premiums lower. Others wanted to specify that plans cover more services.

The law places the burden for MCC compliance upon individuals. It does not prohibit the sale of health plans that fail to meet MCC, nor are employers required to ensure that the plans they offer to employees are MCC-compliant.

Penalties for not obtaining insurance are on a sliding scale based on income. It is tied to the lowest cost (bronze) plan offered by the Connector. Individuals who have not purchased insurance can apply for a financial hardship exemption if they feel they are unable to afford insurance. Exemptions may be granted to those who have faced an extraordinary expense such as a fire or a natural disaster, who have had a period of homelessness, or for whom an essential utility like heat or electricity has been shut off.

In 2008, approximately 26,000 were assessed a penalty, according to the most recent data available from the Connector. An additional 4,000 sought to appeal the penalty. About 5,000 people claimed a religious exemption.[12]

A Change for Business

The controversial mandate, vetoed by Governor Romney and overridden by the Legislature, requiring businesses with 11 or more full-time-equivalent employees (FTEs) to make a "fair and reasonable" contribution to the health insurance of their workers or pay an annual assessment of $295 per employee, was required by statute to go into effect on October 1, 2006.

Additionally, employers with more than 11 or more FTEs were required to offer Section 125 plans as of July 1, 2007. These plans refer to Section 125 of the US Internal Revenue Code, which establishes rules related to taxable and non-taxable benefits offered by employers. Section 125 plans reduce the effective cost of health care coverage for many employees, depending on their total income and family situation, by allowing them to purchase coverage on a pre-tax basis. This administrative mechanism reduces both employees' and employers' share of Medicare and Social Security taxes, as well as employee income taxes and employer unemployment payments.

Employers that do not offer a Section 125 plan can incur a "free-rider" surcharge. This can be applied to companies with 11 or more employees that do not contribute toward or arrange for the purchase of health insurance if their employees use more than $50,000 in free care services in one year. The company can be liable for up to 100 percent of the state-funded hospital costs of employees and their dependents. So far, no one has paid the surcharge.

Under the reform, businesses are prohibited from paying more toward the health insurance of higher-paid employees. They are allowed, however, to contribute more toward the premiums of those who were paid less.

At the time the law was passed, the state did not collect information from individual companies regarding the offer to and enrollment of employees in health insurance plans. This information is now required, which necessitated development of a health insurance reporting and disclosure process.

Fair and Reasonable Defined

One of the most closely watched aspects of the new health care law was how much an employer is actually required to put toward employees' health insurance to avoid facing an assessment.

As with other components of the reform, the definition of "fair and reasonable" was not included in the bill. This was left up to the Division of Health Care Finance and Policy (DHCFP) rather than the Connector Board.

The definition could have far-reaching implications for businesses that might have to adjust their insurance contributions to meet the standard. Some argued that any available health insurance plan should count. Others argued that a minimum standard was necessary. Under the Romney administration, DHCFP determined that businesses with 11 or more employees had to do one of two things: either contribute at least 33 percent of the cost of an employer-sponsored health group plan, or enroll at least 25 percent of their full-time employees in the plan. Given the disagreements, it is not surprising that the definition has been changed over the years since the law has passed.

Covering Low Income Uninsured

One of the concerns that Romney and others pushing for reform raised was the question of how many uninsured individuals were actually working. The concern was that some of these individuals did not have access to insurance even though they had jobs. Part of the solution provided under health care reform was Commonwealth Care, a program that provides subsidized insurance to those with incomes of less than 300 percent of federal poverty level.

The Connector administers the program in consultation with the Office of Medicaid. It is open to adult residents with incomes of less than 300 percent of FPL if they have been state residents for at least six months prior to application and if, in the previous six months, their employer has not provided health insurance for which they are eligible. The employer provisions were included to discourage employers from dropping coverage or otherwise pushing employees to leave a company-sponsored plan in favor of a subsidized option. These provisions were not included in the PPACA.

Eligibility is determined in coordination with MassHealth's (Medicaid) determination procedures. The legislation stipulated that for the first three years of the reform, only plans that currently offered Medicaid managed care plans in the MassHealth program were allowed to offer Commonwealth Care plans; at the time, four plans in total were enrolled in MassHealth. This was intended to help hospitals that ran Medicaid Managed Care Organizations (MMCOs) and also received large amount of free care funding. The expectation was that the funding for the care of low income individuals would shift from the Uncompensated Care Pool to the MMCOs. The three-year exclusivity arrangement gave those hospitals more time to adjust.

Funding for Commonwealth Care came from a number of sources:

redirecting money that had been spent on the uninsured through the Uncompensated Care Pool; new State and Federal matching funds; and penalty payments made by individuals without insurance and employers who incurred a fair share assessment. It was expected that if available funds did not meet the projected costs of enrolling new eligible individuals, enrollment in the program would be suspended.

The plan opened for enrollment in October 2006. There was a rapid 27 percent month-over-month rise in enrollment through February 2008, when growth tapered off. By the end of 2008, there were 162,725 individuals covered through Commonwealth Care. That number dropped to 158,099 by the end of 2010.[13]

Affordability versus Accessibility

The requirements of the Commonwealth Care program have to be carefully balanced. If the premiums for the subsidized program are too high, there is the risk that those who qualify will not participate. If they are set too low, the program could become financially unstable. Having fees set too low would also undermine the principle of "personal responsibility": that everyone who is able to do so should help pay for their coverage. The board initially set premiums ranging from $18 to $106 a month.

A New Insurance Marketplace

In addition to the subsidized program, the reform law created Commonwealth Choice, a marketplace within the Connector for the non-group and small group markets to purchase insurance together.

Before reform, the non-group market, for individuals and families buying insurance on their own, was operating under the rules created during significant reforms made in 1997. Insurers were restricted by law to offering just two types of plans: one with a minimum set of standard benefits and cost sharing levels, and another which, for most insurers, consisted of a similar set of standard benefits (often excluding prescription drugs) and a deductible. Prior to July 1,

2007, these plans had to be offered on a guaranteed issue basis, with continual enrollment. The market operated under a modified community-rated system which did not allow underwriting. The Division of Insurance annually reviewed and approved the premiums.

There were about 42,300 non-group subscribers in 2005.[14] Premiums were prohibitively expensive in the non-group market, which prevented many individuals from purchasing affordable coverage.

The small group market was open to employer groups with up to fifty eligible employees. Insurers were allowed to offer as many health plans as they wanted as long as every plan was available to all small businesses. It also operated under a modified community-rated system.

Under the new Commonwealth Choice program, the Connector defines the plans that will be offered, collects bids from insurance companies and then offers the plans to individuals and small business owners.

Focus on Young Adults

The law included a focus on increasing affordability for health insurance for young adults. Young Adult Plans (YAPs) are available only to Massachusetts residents between the ages of 18 and 26, and offered solely through the Commonwealth Choice program (not available outside the Connector). There was a strong data-driven sense during the reform debate that part of the uninsured problem was that those who were no longer eligible for their parents' health insurance plan, but were generally healthy, were not interested in comprehensive health insurance plans or able to afford them. An entirely separate set of products was created for them.

The benefit package of these products must be "reasonably comprehensive" and include inpatient and outpatient hospital services and physician services for physical and mental illnesses. Insurers may impose coinsurance, deductibles, copayments and tiered provider networks to reduce premiums. They must, however, offer at least one product that includes outpatient drug coverage. This flexibility has resulted in more affordable products compared to the rest of the

Massachusetts market.

Separately, the health care reform law included an expansion of dependent eligibility: allowing young adults to stay on their parents' health insurance until they turn 25 or for two years past their loss of dependent status, whichever is earlier.

MassHealth (Medicaid) Expanded

Health care reform was driven largely by the troubles of the free care pool and the threatened loss of Federal funds for it. A small portion of the reform was an expansion of eligibility for certain populations.

The program expanded MassHealth eligibility to include children in households earning up to 300 percent of FPL. The income limit for participation in the small business-focused Insurance Partnership program was increased to 300 percent from 200 percent of FPL.

The caseload cap for MassHealth Essential, a program for long-term unemployed individuals with less than 133 percent FPL was initially increased to 60,000 from 44,000, and then the enrollment limit was eventually eliminated.

The new law also permanently codified the HIV waiver program for people with incomes up to 200 percent of FPL. Certain benefits for adults including dental, vision, prosthetics, chiropractic care, and level IIIB detoxification were restored. This is one area in which the law was fairly well defined and its implementation more straightforward.

Uncompensated Care Reform

One of the uncontested aspects of health care reform was the decision to restructure the Uncompensated Care Pool. There had been wide agreement that the State's previous provision for covering free care was not effective at either controlling costs or fairly distributing the money among providers.

Under the reform bill, the solution was first to transition funding from this pool to individuals in the form of subsidies for health insurance. Second, the statute reforms the Uncompensated Care Pool to the Health Care Safety Net. As with the Uncompensated Care Pool, the Health Safety Net is supported through a combination of payments from hospitals and insurers along with State and Federal government funds. The newly established Health Safety Net Office within the Division of Health Care Finance and Policy was charged with promulgating regulations pertaining to reimbursable services, standards for medical hardship and the collection of emergency bad debt.

Additionally, the trust fund was expected to continue to spend $6 million annually to fund case management and other demonstration projects aimed at reducing fund liability. These demonstration projects were intended to focus on people with chronic illness, particularly those with substance abuse and psychiatric disorders.

From Debate to Implementation

Governor Romney and legislative leaders, through a contentious debate, ultimately reached a loose consensus on health care reforms. However, they knew the dispute was not over. They had merely outlined goals and set a general direction. The implementation has reflected the disputes and conflicting viewpoints that shaped the original bill and threatened to derail it.

The final bill left significant decision making to the Connector and the DHCFP. The reform should be measured as much by the ongoings of the implementation phase, as by that concepts and ideas contained in the final bill, given the level of latitude provided to implementers.

6

Implementation Defines Health Care Reform

Josh Archambault

Massachusetts Health Reform's New Caretaker: Governor Deval Patrick

In public policy, implementation matters. The previous chapter provides a detailed chronology of the policy and legislative processes that led to Massachusetts' health care reform law. This chapter summarizes the key elements of the reform and explores the important implementation decisions made by Governor Patrick's appointees. Until now, these implementation decisions have not been examined to see how they differ from Governor Romney's decisions and the vision outlined during the original policy debate.

The 2006 statute served as a framework which left many policy decisions to the implementation phase. An understanding of the implementation sheds light on the next chapter's reform outcomes.

Implementation of the provisions of the 2006 legislation was dramatically affected by who was in office at the time. Some regulations promulgated by Governor Romney were modified by the Patrick administration when he took power on January 4, 2007; in these cases, it is easy to see different ideologies in play. Other regulatory decisions were not made until after Governor Romney's tenure, so it is more difficult to know how he would have implemented certain provisions. Nonetheless, information from the policy debate can help to inform this discussion.

Individual Mandate

Provision

Beginning January 1, 2008, all residents of the Commonwealth aged 18 and older were required to obtain and maintain a minimum level of health insurance coverage. People who do not purchase health insurance or enroll in the appropriate health insurance program face penalties if insurance coverage is deemed affordable for them. The legislation left the policy decision of what would be deemed affordable to those who would implement the law. Residents submit proof of coverage to the state's Department of Revenue and are permitted to appeal any state determination of health insurance affordability.

During the legislative process, the concept of minimum creditable coverage (MCC) emerged in discussions about the level of insurance coverage necessary to meet the individual mandate. The statute required that individuals had to meet what was a then-undefined level of minimum creditable coverage with the purchase of their insurance, or be enrolled in a government health program or other niche arrangement to avoid the loss of a state income tax exemption or other penalties under the individual mandate.[1] The specific definition of MCC was left to the board of the Health Connector to decide.

Implementation

Governor Romney supported a mandate that required a minimum level of coverage, in particular, for catastrophic events.[2] This mandate emerged in response to the federal Emergency Medical Treatment and Active Labor Act (EMTALA) which required hospitals to screen and stabilize patients without regard to insurance coverage; often leaving taxpayers holding the bill. Therefore, the original 2005 legislation filed by Governor Romney required that Massachusetts residents carry, at a minimum, catastrophic medical coverage, or in lieu of such coverage, a $10,000 bond with the State Treasurer's office to pay for medical care, an approach that tracked the Commonwealth's requirement for automobile insurance coverage. However, this provision was left out of the final bill. Instead, legislators added placeholder language requiring the Connector to define MCC, which occurred after the Romney administration left office.

Following the transition from the Romney administration to the Patrick administration, there were significant ex officio changes on the Connector board. The reconstituted board took up the challenge of defining minimum creditable coverage, taking a heavy-handed prescriptive approach. The biggest disagreement came over whether drug coverage should be required as part of the MCC definition. Business groups and others felt this requirement would drive up the cost of plans and preclude affordability. Others felt that without drug coverage, those with insurance would remain financially vulnerable. The day the Connector board was supposed to vote on the issue, business groups went public with their concerns that many residents who already had insurance (that presumably met their health care needs and budget) would have to upgrade to meet the state's new standard. At the time, it was estimated that there were approximately 160,000 residents who had plans that would not have met the new MCC definition because of the drug benefit requirement. The board ultimately voted unanimously to include a drug benefit, but delayed the implementation of the requirement to give businesses (which were not required to comply but would undoubtedly receive pressure from employees) and individuals more time to meet the terms of the new standards.

The standards have been revised somewhat over time. As of 2010, the MCC standards require that individuals carry insurance that offers coverage for a broad range of medical services including outpatient surgery, diagnostic imaging, maternity care, prescription drugs, and chemotherapy. In addition, the plans must cover preventive care doctor's visits without a deductible. There is a cap on annual deductibles of $2,000 for an individual and $4,000 for a family for in-network services. For plans with up-front deductibles or co-insurance on core services, the standards require an annual maximum on out-of-pocket spending of no more than $5,000 for an individual and $10,000 for a family for services received in-network. There can be no caps on total benefits for a particular illness or for a single year. For policies that have a separate prescription drug deductible, it cannot exceed $250 for an individual or $500 for a family. In 2011, the Connector board made an additional revision that prohibited plans from applying a fixed dollar cap on prescription drug benefits.

Anecdotes have emerged about individuals who were satisfied with catastrophic-only health insurance coverage prior to the establishment of the minimum creditable coverage who have chosen to drop their private-pay insurance in favor of the publicly subsidized Commonwealth Care insurance program, or have been forced to buy insurance benefits to comply with the minimum creditable coverage standards. Clearly, the current MCC standards do not conform to the previous administration's more minimalist philosophy.

Employer Responsibility: Defining a "Fair and Reasonable Contribution"

Provision

Under the legislation, employers with 11 or more full-time-equivalent employees must facilitate pre-tax availability of health insurance coverage for their employees. In addition, employers with 11 or more full-time-equivalent employees that do not make a "fair and reasonable" contribution toward employee health insurance premiums are charged an annual per employee fee of no more than $295 (or $73.75 quarterly). This figure was loosely tied to the per person amount of care funded by the Uncompensated Care Pool for people who were employed but not covered by an employer plan. In the 2006 law, the Division of Health Care Finance and Policy (DHCFP), the state agency that managed the Uncompensated Care Pool, was required to define what constituted a "fair and reasonable" contribution from employers towards health insurance.

Implementation

The mandate that employers make a "fair and reasonable" contribution to employee health insurance was consistently opposed by the Romney administration, leading to a veto in the final bill that was later overridden by the Legislature. Under the Romney administration, the DHCFP promulgated Fair Share Contribution (FSC) regulations. Businesses with 11 or more employees were required either to contribute at least 33 percent of the cost of an employer-sponsored health insurance group plan (the minimum contribution required by carriers for family plans at the time), or enroll at least 25 percent of their full-time employees in the plan. Although the employer requirements were not supported by the business community, this interpretation of the statute was felt to be "business-friendly."

However, soon after Deval Patrick took office, his appointees attempted to raise the requirement on all employers by changing the word "or" to "and" in the regulation. After significant pushback from small businesses, the administration relented and changed the definition to apply only to employers with 50 or more employees. Companies with 50 or more employees now must fulfill both tests unless 75 percent of employees are enrolled; if so, the 33 percent contribution level does not apply.

This simple word change had a significant impact on certain businesses. Specifically, this change is more challenging for companies with large numbers of part-time employees, or those with employees who receive insurance through their spouses or Medicare. Even if these companies contribute more than 33 percent of the cost of insurance, which many do, they may not meet the enrollment requirements to avoid the penalties.

In addition, the Patrick administration amended the definition of "full-time employee" to include anyone who worked enough hours to qualify for full-time health benefits. Initially, a full-time-equivalent employee was anyone who worked 35 hours or more per week. This was revised, effective January 1, 2009, to include as a full-time-equivalent employee anyone who worked the lesser of 35 hours or more per week or the number of weekly payroll hours to be eligible for the employer's full-time health benefits. The definition of a full-time worker is a particular concern for seasonal businesses that may have full-time employees for only part of the year.

The administration also increased the frequency with which businesses have to report data to the state. When the full-time-employee regulation first went into effect, employers were required to calculate and report compliance on an annual basis. The Patrick administration changed this to a quarterly reporting requirement, effective January 1, 2009.

The end result of these changes has been that the firms required to pay the "Fair Share Penalty" under the current regulatory rules are typically temporary help services, security guard and patrol services, janitorial services, restaurants, and other service-oriented industries. The state assesses penalties of roughly $17 million annually on these employers for not meeting this standard.[3]

Establishment of New Premium Support

Provision

In the 2006 reform, some money, in the form of premium subsidies for low-income individuals, was redirected from the soon to be restructured Uncompensated Care Pool to the newly created Commonwealth Care health insurance program. The Connector was required to establish a sliding-scale subsidy schedule for eligible beneficiaries. However, the statute specified that individuals with an income up to 100 percent of the federal poverty level (FPL) ($10,210) would have similar cost sharing to those on Medicaid,[4] and that the subsidy payments would be paid directly to eligible health insurance plans by the Connector.

Implementation

In formulating their proposal, the Romney administration envisioned an insurance model that emphasized individual choice and responsibility. As part of that philosophy, the Romney administration planned to have some cost sharing for all income levels, albeit cost sharing that was nominal at the lower end of the income scale.

The approach implemented by the Connector board in the years following passage included full premium subsidies (free insurance) for participants with incomes up to 150 percent of the FPL ($15,315). For those earning 151-200 percent of FPL, the monthly premiums were reduced from $40 to $35. These changes were expected to eliminate premiums for an estimated 29,000 low-income residents and reduce premiums for another 23,000.[5] The board cited the administrative costs associated with collecting small dollar payments as one reason for not charging users, which may be true, but the policy voided the goal of individual participation and responsibility.

As of the end of 2011, the Connector provides subsidies towards the purchase of private health insurance products for adults with incomes below 300% FPL. Full subsidies are available for those with incomes less than 150% of the FPL,[6] with sliding scale subsidies available to those with incomes that are 150-300% of the FPL. Finally, the Connector board has also made a policy decision to maintain coverage for certain individuals who do not pay their premiums, even if they make enough to be required to, by transferring them into the lowest cost zero-premium category.

The Connector as Market Facilitator for Small Businesses and Individuals: Commonwealth Choice

Provision

The Connector was created to help address significant market failures affecting the purchase of health care insurance such as the lack of access to innovative, value-driven health plans for small businesses and their employees, as well as the individual market's economic irrationality (and related adverse selection issues), caused largely by previous legislative intervention. As passed, the health care reform legislation, which merged the non- and small group markets, by default removed some of the regulation from the non-group market. The law merged the non-group and small-group markets and created the mandate-lite Young Adult Plans (YAP) for people 16-19 years of age. The process by which insurance carriers would be allowed to sell insurance through the Connector (the so-called Seal of Approval process) was to be defined after the passage of the law.[7]

Implementation

The Romney administration had envisioned an unsubsidized exchange program that provided small employers with a healthy defined contribution model. In this model, employees would be given a broad range of insurance options ranging from catastrophic to robust benefit plans. Under this model, the employer would simply contribute a defined dollar amount to employees, and employees would choose a plan that met their needs. The model's goals were to move the current employer-based system to an individual purchase decision and encourage competition and consumerism.

In July 2007, the Connector launched the Commonwealth Choice program for individuals to purchase non-subsidized insurance plans.[8] Commonwealth Choice serves as a clear example of how policy decisions made during implementation by the Connector often limited choice and competition for small businesses. For example, the decision to enact high minimum creditable coverage standards was followed by the organization of plans into tiers of Gold, Silver, and Bronze, which limited the diversity of offerings. The tiered system was a creation of the Connector which was not included in the original law. All three tiers had to provide comprehensive coverage, including inpatient and outpatient medical care, emergency care, mental health and substance abuse services, rehabilitation services, hospice, and vision care.[9]

What resulted was a set of almost identical benefit packages from the seven approved insurance carriers, with the major differentiation being the levels of cost sharing through co-pays, co-insurance, and deductibles. These decisions made the Connector into a health insurance sales channel that was indistinguishable from what was already being offered in the general marketplace, thereby limiting its appeal to small business owners.

Next, the small business program, Contributory Plan (CP), the Connector's version of a defined contribution model, was launched in 2009 after several delays. The CP limited small businesses to offering their employees only those plans in a single metallic tier, moving even farther away from the original vision of an open marketplace, and severely limiting the diversity of consumer options.[10] The CP pilot program was not the vision of the Romney administration, whose intention was to give employees more freedom to choose with significant variation in insurance design, rather than being restricted by their employer's choice. The Connector's failure to put in place a true defined contribution program that provided employees with a range of insurance coverage options was another obstacle to attracting small business customers and realizing the original vision of a functioning marketplace.

The initial goal for the CP was to sign up 100 small businesses but it attracted just 65, after which enrollment was frozen. The CP was subsequently suspended in favor of a new plan called Business Express, launched in February 2010. This new plan offers just seven options, far fewer than the Contributory Plan. Importantly, employees are not offered a choice of products; the employer chooses the product and employees enroll in that product.

Business Express reduces the monthly fees paid to third-party administrators for employers with fewer than five employees. It does not address the underlying drivers of rising health insurance costs for small businesses. In general, small businesses have been able to get plans on the open market for the same, or a lower price, than they can through the Connector. Despite the state's ability to hold annual premium rate hikes for the subsidized Commonwealth Care plans to around 5 percent, rates for small businesses have increased, on average, 15 percent per year annually over the past five years.[11]

The Connector also requires employers to meet the same requirements as every business outside the exchange, including contributing at least 50 percent towards employee premiums and meeting carrier participation rules. Companies with five or fewer employees must have 100 percent participation from their employees and those with six or more must have participation of at least 75 percent.[12] These requirements were the very barriers which the Romney administration wanted to eliminate and had identified before passage of the law. There has been limited interest in the non-subsidized marketplace. While many major Massachusetts insurers are under contract with the Connector to offer plans in the Commonwealth Choice market, some have refused to participate in reaction to regulatory decisions made by the Patrick administration.[13] As a result, the Connector has failed to capture economies of scale (in the non-subsidized market) for insurers and to offer enhanced choice to employers and employees.

The Seal of Approval process, established by the Connector, has also limited the number of insurers selling in the Connector. The process was put in place to ensure that the plans met minimum standards and provided appropriate levels of coverage. Instead, the approval process has resulted in a more uniform set of offerings with differentiation based largely on actuarial value, not design features.

In general, disagreements or complaints from small businesses over the Commonwealth Choice program have centered on the limited number and variety of plans offered as well as the premiums. However, the Connector is not solely responsible, as all pre-reform state insurance mandates are still in place and others have been added by the Legislature. Small businesses carry the burden of mandates most directly, since larger self-insured companies are exempt from these state mandates. Excessive mandates limit what insurers can offer in the newly merged small business and individual market. Paired with the Connector's general tendency toward standardizing plans, consumers have been given limited choice, and many pay more than they would have under a Romney-run Connector.

Uncompensated Care Pool Reform (Health Safety Net)

Provision

Several changes were made to the system for treating people who remained uninsured in the 2006 reform law. The Uncompensated Care Pool, or "free care pool," was eliminated and a new program, the Health Safety Net, was established. The intent was to eliminate fee-for-service bulk payments to institutions based on historical uncompensated care levels, and replace them with a new payment system more in line with the overall philosophy of the reform, whereby money follows an individual, not an institution. The reform's intention was to reduce utilization volume and the costs of the Health Safety Net as more residents obtained insurance coverage.

The new payment system is based on Medicare principles and requires providers to submit claims for reimbursement. Inpatient services are paid using hospital-specific rates adjusted for variations in patient acuity, teaching status, and percent of low-income patients, while outpatient services are paid using a per-visit rate developed by estimating the amount Medicare would have paid for comparable service. In addition, eligible services are aligned with those in the Medicaid program, which, in some cases, require prior approval or adherence to certain formularies. Finally, new program features ensure that people are enrolled in the coverage for which they are eligible before they are permitted to use the Health Safety Net.

Implementation

The reform of the uncompensated care pool began under Governor Patrick. Following a predicted significant decline in free care pool utilization after reform, demand began to grow in 2010. A slow economy may be partly to blame, but there also have been instances when policy decisions about other programs may have increased the use of the Health Safety Net.

In 2009, due to budgetary concerns, the Connector and the Patrick administration closed the Commonwealth Care program to legal immigrants who have been in the United States for less than five years. Individuals already enrolled in the program were transitioned into a new program called Commonwealth Care Bridge, and future enrollment was capped. Any new legal immigrants applying for benefits may now be eligible for the Health Safety

Net as they are restricted from enrolling in Commonwealth Care Bridge.[14] In addition, in July 2010, MassHealth (Medicaid) and Commonwealth Care dental benefits were restructured, and as a result the Health Safety Net now covers certain dental services for members of those two programs.

A troubling recent audit of the Health Safety Net by the Inspector General of Massachusetts found tens of millions of dollars in claims being paid for out-of-state residents, medically unnecessary services, duplicate payments for the same services for the same patients, and payments for medically unlikely events.[15]

Before reform, the fund was spending around $700 million annually. The cost of the program decreased to $396 million in 2008 but demand has since grown to $475 million in 2010. Demand, however, represents only what providers would have been paid in the absence of a funding shortfall. Because demand exceeded program funding, hospitals experienced a $70 million shortfall in 2010, and the fund only paid out $405 million.[16]

Although never a fully developed policy, Romney administration officials had envisioned eventually turning the Health Safety Net into a fixed pool of funds for which a standing committee of state health care officials would review institutional grant funding proposals.

Health Care Quality and Cost Council (HCQCC)

Provision

The HCQCC was added to the 2006 reform during the legislative debate. The Massachusetts state senate established HCQCC as a semi-independent agency made up of governor-appointed subject matter experts and state officials. The Council's mission includes improving health care quality, containing costs, and reducing racial and ethnic disparities. Additionally, the HCQCC is tasked with disseminating quality and cost information to the general public.[17]

Implementation

While the Council was staffed shortly after the law was signed, the Patrick administration has demonstrated a lack of interest in fully staffing or empowering the independent Council to drive reform. The work of the Council has suffered as a result. Out of frustration, the Legislature reconstituted the Council in 2010 legislation, requiring the Chair to be elected in an effort to kick-start the HCQCC.[18] One of the original visions for the HCQCC was to allow consumers to use cost and quality data when selecting a health insurance plan in the Connector, but this has not come to pass. Pioneer Institute has discussed in-depth the challenges and shortcoming of the transparency efforts in previous work.[19] As a result, both mechanisms envisioned to help control costs, HCQCC and a robust defined contribution system have yet to be realized. If the Council had been able to drive reform efforts, consumers obtaining insurance within the Connector could have become value-seeking purchasers with cost and quality information available as they decided on plans to purchase with their employer contribution.

Merging of Small Group and Non-Group Markets

Provision

The 2006 legislation required the merging of the small group and non-group insurance markets to create one risk pool to facilitate lower costs for individuals and families purchasing insurance without employer subsidies. This merge helped to remove some regulation on the non-group market that had left it dysfunctional. Years before, the legislature had intervened layering mandated regulations on products to be sold in the non-group market. The result of such action was only two insurance products being sold in the non-group market. The merged market would allow individuals to purchase insurance at a price that was similar to those in the much larger pre-merged small group market.

Implementation

The Romney administration proposed this provision, and it was implemented largely as planned, resulting in an initial decline in premiums for many individuals purchasing insurance in this newly merged market. The most promising effort to save money for small businesses in the original reform was the Connector's Commonwealth Choice program.

MassHealth (Medicaid) Expansion

Provision

The legislation expanded MassHealth coverage, through the State Children's Health Insurance Program (SCHIP) program, to children in families who earn between 200% and 300% of the FPL. It also expanded eligibility to 300% of the FPL for the Insurance Partnership Program to previously uninsured individuals working for small firms (<50 employees) and removed enrollment caps on various smaller programs. The bill restored optional federal benefits to MassHealth adults that had been cut in 2002, including dental, dentures, vision, chiropractic, certain prosthetics, and orthotic devices. Finally, dental coverage for those on MassHealth Essential, a program for long-term unemployed individuals, and legal immigrants previously removed from MassHealth, were added.

Implementation

Governor Romney vetoed the provisions that expanded optional benefits in the MassHealth population and allowed legal immigrants back onto MassHealth; both vetoes were overridden by the Legislature. Otherwise, the Medicaid expansion was straightforward and implemented by the state shortly after it received the federal waiver to do so. Within five years of the law's passage, outreach efforts along with a poor economy caused enrollment to grow by

252,000, or 24 percent, for a total 1,307,000 members.[20] Expansions in the reform law accounted for 61,000 of those new members. The rest would have been eligible prior to reform, and these enrollees have joined the program largely due to the poor economy. However, outreach efforts may have helped to attract them to the program, or the new individual mandate may have spurred them to sign up.

From Debate to Implementation, Now to Evaluation

Health care reform started with the personal mandate, a measure on which there was broad agreement and which has been widely accepted. One open question and controversial aspect was the level of insurance required. The state has moved toward having more rather than fewer mandated service options than Romney and others envisioned.

The unsubsidized Commonwealth Choice has been implemented largely in a manner to diminish choice for employees, and it is more restrictive than many of the original architects hoped for.

With the requirement that employers make a "fair and reasonable" contribution towards their employees' health insurance, significant leeway was originally given to the method by which companies would be deemed compliant. Although, during the five years of implementation, the requirements on companies have increased substantially. Small businesses, in particular, have felt the burden of these decisions, and state-mandated benefits have increased their cost burden, while larger self-insured companies are exempt from these state mandates.

The true measure of whether the reality of reform lived up to the hope expressed in Faneuil Hall and on Beacon Hill in 2006 should be understood by examining both the original vision of the reform, and on the outcomes of the past five years' implementation decisions. Only further and continued data analysis will lead us to a better understanding of the true impact of the law and its implementation.

7

Evaluating the Massachusetts Experiment: The Data

Amy Lischko & Josh Archambault

It takes the distance of a few years to understand any reform. Pioneer Institute waited until 2009 to begin evaluating Massachusetts' 2006 law entitled "An Act Providing Access to Affordable, Quality, Accountable Health Care."[1] Many opinions have been formed and advanced, by those on both sides of the ideological spectrum, on the impact of the law. Some have insisted that the law led to a collapse in small business confidence, long wait lines to see a provider, and lower quality care; others have, in essence, insisted that insurance translates into better health outcomes and have waved off the significance of new burdens on small businesses. The fact is that only now, in 2012, are we starting to get a clearer and fuller picture of the impact of a reform that reshaped significant aspects of the Massachusetts health care system. Many questions remain unanswered, and in some areas of interest, the data remain sparse.

The goals of the legislation were to make health insurance affordable to almost every resident and establish mechanisms to help control health care inflation. The legislation reformed the health care system by focusing on the role of the individual. Specifically, the law eliminated some of the barriers to purchasing health insurance, transitioned existing government assistance from hospitals to the individual in the form of subsidies to purchase health insurance, encouraged personal responsibility, and attempted to contain health care costs.

Pioneer Institute's assessment framework, developed in 2009, focused on four major areas: barriers to access, equitable financing, administrative efficiency, and efficacy and efficiency of the quality of care.[2] For each of these areas, Pioneer proposed a series of metrics that would allow for a comprehensive evaluation of the reform. With time, this analysis method has been reassessed and adjusted due to data quality and availability.

Massachusetts in 2012

Three points are worth making in drawing lessons about the empirical impact of the 2006 Massachusetts health law. First, the analyses that follow depict outcomes attributable not only to the law's provisions but also to the implementation of the law between 2006 and 2011. For those seeking quick political takeaways during a presidential campaign season, the following analyses will not satisfy their political hunger.

Like any law, the Massachusetts health care legislation had flexibility and options built into it – some by design, others out of political necessity. As the Patrick administration put its own stamp onto the reform many of the market-based aspects of the legislation were given little weight. Over time, the organizing principle of health care reform moved away from the consumer and small business owner toward the subsidized products offered by the Connector. Our analyses look at reality in 2012, six years after the passage of the Massachusetts law. It is impossible to empirically separate the impact of the implementation phase from the legislative phase of the law.

Second, the desire to draw direct comparisons to other state and federal laws based on these data must be tempered by the recognition that Massachusetts has unique cultural characteristics. The Commonwealth not only has a history of attempts at health care reform, the 2006 reform being the Bay State's third attempt at comprehensive health reform, but its business culture is in many ways unique. Massachusetts companies have a strong tradition of offering health insurance, which largely accounted for the roughly 92 percent insured rate *before* reform. Massachusetts also has a number of characteristics that are not shared by other states: the state is high income, geographically compact, and home to numerous academic medical facilities.

Finally, for those who would compare the Massachusetts law to the 2010 federal law, any fact-based appraisal would have to note that they differ greatly in terms of financing, complexity, magnitude, and guiding rules and regulations that govern subsidies and access to a health insurance exchange.

Access

Prior to 2006, Massachusetts had been a leader among states in providing health care and health care coverage to its population. Employers in Massachusetts have consistently had one of the highest offer rates in the nation. In addition, Massachusetts had a strong safety net, including a generous Medicaid program and a network of safety net providers – community health

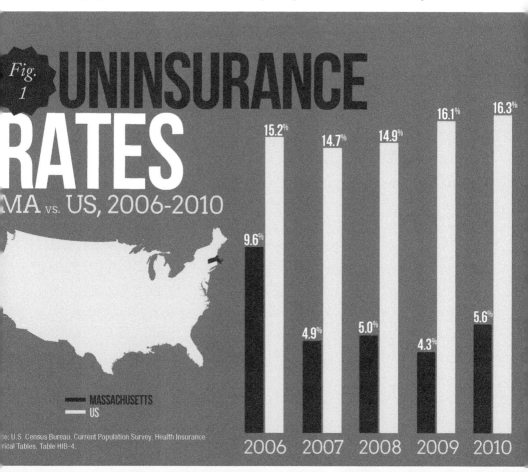

Fig. 1 **UNINSURANCE RATES**

MA vs. US, 2006-2010

MASSACHUSETTS
US

Source: U.S. Census Bureau, Current Population Survey, Health Insurance Historical Tables, Table HIB-4.

	2006	2007	2008	2009	2010
US	15.2%	14.7%	14.9%	16.1%	16.3%
Massachusetts	9.6%	4.9%	5.0%	4.3%	5.6%

centers and hospitals – that provided care to low-income uninsured individuals largely reimbursed through the Commonwealth's Uncompensated Care Pool (UCP).

Access can be thought of in two ways: access to insurance coverage and access to health care services. One of the primary goals of the reform was to increase access to insurance coverage so that people would have increased access to primary care and preventive services and not rely on hospitals and emergency departments for care.

Access to Coverage

Number of Uninsured over Time

There remain discrepancies regarding the overall number of uninsured, all survey results, gathered by both national and state entities, indicate that

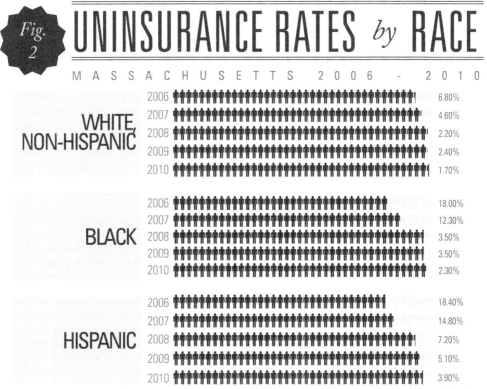

Fig. 2 — UNINSURANCE RATES *by* RACE

MASSACHUSETTS 2006 - 2010

WHITE, NON-HISPANIC
2006	6.80%
2007	4.60%
2008	2.20%
2009	2.40%
2010	1.70%

BLACK
2006	18.00%
2007	12.30%
2008	3.50%
2009	3.50%
2010	2.30%

HISPANIC
2006	18.40%
2007	14.80%
2008	7.20%
2009	5.10%
2010	3.90%

Source: DHCFP, Massachusetts Household Survey on Health Insurance Status 2007 • DHCFP, Massachusetts Household Surveys - Detailed Tabulations: 2008, 2009, 2010.

Massachusetts has reduced its rate of uninsurance. Although state surveys record lower levels of uninsured. Figure 1 presents data from the Census Bureau so that the uninsured rate in Massachusetts can be compared over time and to the rate for the United States over the same time period. The reduction in the uninsured occurred across all races and ethnicities, although Hispanics and blacks still have higher rates of uninsurance than whites (Figure 2).

From these data it can be concluded that the health reform legislation has been successful in reducing the number of uninsured in Massachusetts. The estimate of uninsured was reduced from 651,000 in 2006 to 370,000 (from 9.6 to 5.6 percent) in 2010, a decrease of 281,000. Uninsured rates for children were reduced from 7 to 3 percent (not shown).

Total Health Safety Net Users and Cost

Increasing access to affordable insurance coverage for most residents should lead to a reduction in free or uncompensated care provided by hospitals and community health centers. Therefore, a significant amount of funding from the safety net was redirected to instead pay for subsidies for lower-income residents to purchase private insurance.

Because of the generous subsidy program and the mandate to carry insurance, the trajectory for safety-net funding was expected to drop substantially as reform was implemented. Moving forward, the hope was that the rate of increase for free care would parallel rates of medical inflation, assuming everyone remained covered. As shown in Figures 3 and 4, an initial several-year drop in demand occurred, but demand has increased in terms of both cost and volume of visits over the past two years. The current administration has not established an effective audit and verification system, making it hard to understand the causes of this increase in demand. Massachusetts has also seen an increase in the number of users of the safety net who report no income: 37 percent of users in fiscal year 2005 to 45 percent in fiscal year 2010, accounting for 54 percent of payments (not shown).

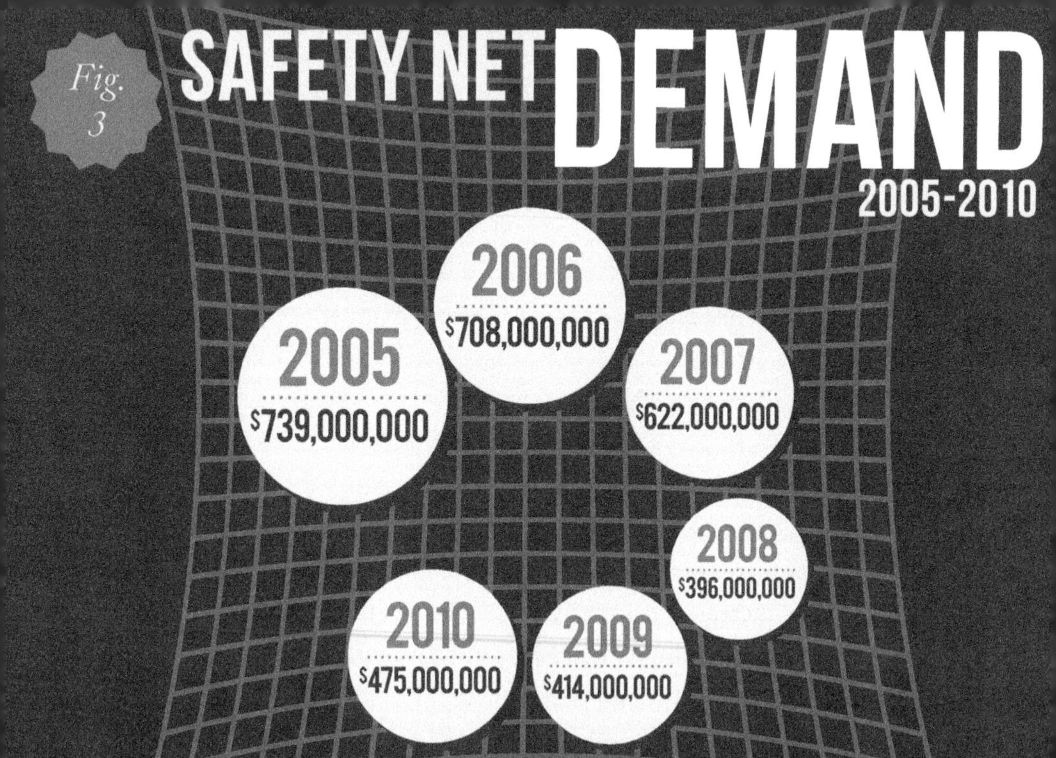

Fig. 3

SAFETY NET DEMAND
2005-2010

2005
$739,000,000

2006
$708,000,000

2007
$622,000,000

2008
$396,000,000

2010
$475,000,000

2009
$414,000,000

Note: The Health Safety Net is meant to cover medically necessary services and reimburses hospitals and community health centers for a portion of the cost of reimbursable health services provided to low-income, uninsured or underinsured residents.
Sources: 2005, 2006, and 2007, DHCFP, Uncompensated Care Pool Annual Report. And 2008, 2009, and 2010, DHCFP, Annual Report, Health Safety Net.

Fig. 4

NUMBER OF SAFETY NET USERS

445,210 — 2006
422,495 — 2007
262,000 — 2008
274,000 — 2009
315,000 — 2010

Note: The Health Safety Net is meant to cover medically necessary services and reimburses hospitals and community health centers for a portion of the cost of reimbursable health services provided to low-income, uninsured or underinsured residents.
Source: DHCFP, Uncompensated Care Pool Annual Report, 2006, 2007. DHCFP, Health Safety Net Annual Report, 2008, 2009, 2010.

Emergency Department Utilization

Many believe that when access to insurance is improved, one would expect to see a decrease in the use of the emergency department (ED), particularly for conditions that can be treated in a primary care setting. Recent synthesis of the literature, however, casts some doubt on this thesis and suggests that "expansion of health insurance coverage on its own is likely to increase rather than decrease stress on overcrowded EDs."[3] There is some evidence of this phenomenon in Massachusetts. As shown in Figure 5, ED visits have increased since the reform, although the rate of increase has declined. A recent study by the Commonwealth found that ED visits increased primarily for conditions that could have been treated in a primary care setting,[4] including visits for mental health conditions. State data also shows that the most frequent visitors to the ED have Medicaid and Commonwealth Care coverage (not shown). New survey data from the Blue Cross Blue Shield of Massachusetts Foundation documents a small decrease in

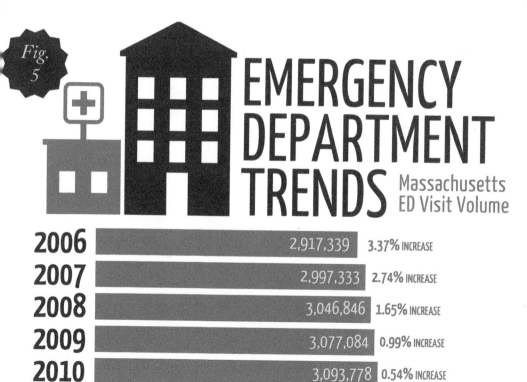

Fig. 5

EMERGENCY DEPARTMENT TRENDS
Massachusetts ED Visit Volume

Year	Volume	Increase
2006	2,917,339	3.37% INCREASE
2007	2,997,333	2.74% INCREASE
2008	3,046,846	1.65% INCREASE
2009	3,077,084	0.99% INCREASE
2010	3,093,778	0.54% INCREASE

Source: Division of Health Care Finance and Policy, Massachusetts Emergency Department Visit Volume, FY 2010, 2009, 2008, 2007, 2006.

The Great Experiment

self-reported visits to an ED for the non-elderly in 2010.[5]

Access to Health Care Services

While access to health insurance is important, access to care and improvements in overall health are the ultimate goals of any health reform initiative. In particular, increasing access to primary care and preventive services has the potential to lower costs, yield better outcomes, and reduce the demand for more expensive health care services.

Utilization Rates of Preventive Care Services

An increase in insurance coverage should also lead to an increase in the utilization of preventive services. However, any increases in the utilization of preventive services may also be the result of other initiatives such as education and outreach or other broader quality improvement efforts. For this analysis,

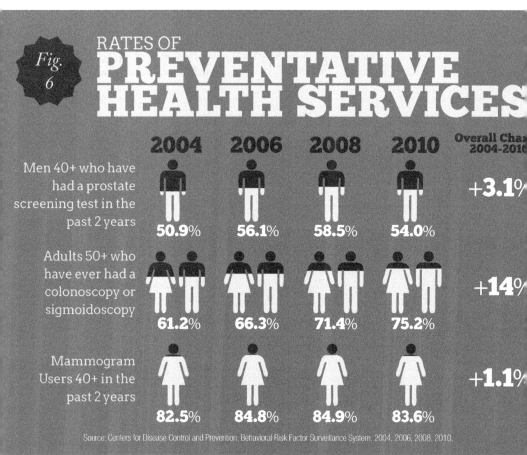

Fig. 6

RATES OF **PREVENTATIVE HEALTH SERVICES**

	2004	2006	2008	2010	Overall Change 2004-2010
Men 40+ who have had a prostate screening test in the past 2 years	50.9%	56.1%	58.5%	54.0%	+3.1%
Adults 50+ who have ever had a colonoscopy or sigmoidoscopy	61.2%	66.3%	71.4%	75.2%	+14%
Mammogram Users 40+ in the past 2 years	82.5%	84.8%	84.9%	83.6%	+1.1%

Source: Centers for Disease Control and Prevention; Behavioral Risk Factor Surveillance System; 2004, 2006, 2008, 2010.

rates of three common screening procedures are assessed before and after the reform: prostate screening in men age 40 and above in the past two years, colonoscopy or sigmoidoscopy of people over 50 years old, and mammography in women age 40 and above in the past two years. As shown in Figure 6, prostate-screening rates increased slightly following the passage of reform but have decreased more recently, rates for colonoscopy/sigmoidoscopy were significantly improved post- reform, and rates for mammography remained constant pre-post reform.

It is possible that newly insured people initially had difficulty getting access to a primary care physician to learn about and schedule preventive screenings. The percent of adults reporting having a regular physician has increased only slightly since the reform, as shown in Figure 7.

Average wait times for scheduling an appointment with a family or internal medicine physician increased directly following the reform but have been in flux from year to year and at times have decreased (Figure 8). Wait times differ

Fig. 7

ADULT RESIDENTS
who have a
HEALTH CARE PROVIDER

87% 88% 88% 89% 90% 89%

2004 2006 2007 2008 2009 2010

Source: DHCFP, Health Care in Massachusetts: Key Indicators, May 2011.

significantly, as they did before reform, based largely on the area of practice and the geographic location of a patient. Of potential concern is the decreasing percentage of internal and family physicians accepting new patients since reform (Figure 8). Some decrease over time was expected as more individuals gained insurance coverage, but it will be important to monitor access over time.

Summary of Access Results

The primary goal of the reform was to increase access to insurance and primary care. Without question, the reform increased insurance coverage. Yet, what is less clear is whether this increase in coverage has improved access to primary and preventive care. Emergency Department rates for primary care treatable conditions have increased since the reform, preventive screenings have not increased significantly but more adults do report having a personal health care provider post-reform. From these data, it is clear that providing access to insurance may be a required first step in improving access to care, but

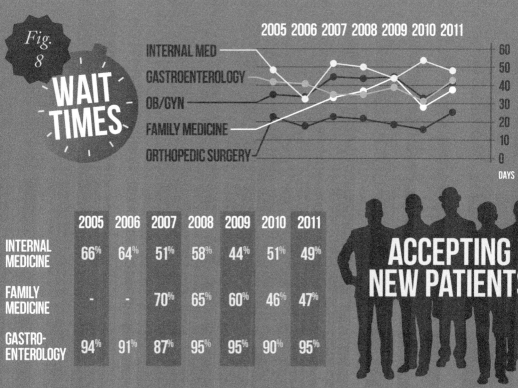

Fig. 8

WAIT TIMES

2005 2006 2007 2008 2009 2010 2011

INTERNAL MED
GASTROENTEROLOGY
OB/GYN
FAMILY MEDICINE
ORTHOPEDIC SURGERY

60
50
40
30
20
10
0
DAYS

ACCEPTING NEW PATIENTS

	2005	2006	2007	2008	2009	2010	2011
INTERNAL MEDICINE	66%	64%	51%	58%	44%	51%	49%
FAMILY MEDICINE	-	-	70%	65%	60%	46%	47%
GASTRO-ENTEROLOGY	94%	91%	87%	95%	95%	90%	95%

Source: Massachusetts Medical Society, 2011 Patient Access to Health Care Study: A Survey of Massachusetts Physicians' Offices, 2011 Physician Workforce Study

other incentives may be necessary to change health care-seeking behaviors and improve the availability of health care professionals.

Cost

Rising health care costs have consistently made headlines throughout the past two decades. When compared to the rest of the nation, the problem of increased spending on health care was particularly acute in Massachusetts. Prior to the reform, Massachusetts' health care costs exceeded national averages and were growing at faster rates than the nation overall. For example, Massachusetts' 2004 per capita health expenditure of $6,683 was 27% greater than the national average of $5,283.[6] Health care spending from 2000 to 2004 grew by 7.4% in Massachusetts, compared with 6.9% nationally.[7]

Through the reform, Massachusetts hoped to constrain health care costs for consumers, employers, and the government in a number of ways. For consumers, prior to the reform, Massachusetts had a generous safety net providing free care

Fig. 9 — INDIVIDUAL PREMIUMS IN NON-GROUP MARKET

~ PER MONTH ~

2006	2007	2008	2009	2010*
$437	$379	$369	$383	$437

'010 data is taken from Kaiser Family Foundation, Average Per Person Monthly Premiums in the Individual Market.

ate: The non-group market is a segment of the health insurance market where customers are purchasing insurance on an individual basis. The 2006 non-group premium is in the pre-merger market, and should only be loosely compared to the 2007, 2008, 2009, and 2010 premiums for individuals that chose to join the merged market. Some ividuals decided to remain in pre-merged non-group market.

at hospitals and community health centers for people under 200% FPL (federal poverty level) and partial free care for people earning 200- 400% FPL. For people purchasing through their employers, insurance coverage was also generous, with the average employer contributing 80% of an individual policy and 75% of a family policy. However, for people purchasing in the non-group market, coverage was expensive. As one of the few states with a remaining guaranteed-issue policy and partial community rating bands, the individual market was prohibitively expensive for most people.

The reform helped low-to-moderate income consumers purchasing insurance on their own by providing subsidies for insurance coverage. For those with incomes above 300% FPL the reform merged the non-group and small-employer markets, creating a larger pool over which to spread risk and lower rates.

For employers, the Health Insurance Connector Authority (Connector) was established by the law to assist businesses in acquiring affordable, high-quality health care coverage. In addition, the law hoped to mitigate cost shifting that was occurring from public to private payers (employers) by insuring more people. The law also featured increased Medicaid rates for some providers to show commitment to this goal of reducing cost shifting. Due to budgetary pressures the current administration and legislature have not fulfilled that commitment.

It was determined that with little additional cost to the state, Massachusetts could use funding currently being spent on the safety net to fund subsidies to individuals. A federal waiver meant that the federal government would cover approximately fifty percent of the costs. Subsidizing coverage as opposed to paying for expensive episodes of care was thought to be a more equitable and cost-effective use of government funding.

Costs – To Individuals

The merging of the individual and small-group markets provided some premium relief to individuals purchasing in this market (Figure 9). In addition, for people between the ages of 19 and 26, Young Adult Plans (YAP), offered through the Connector, provide the choice of a slimmed-down benefit plan at a more affordable price. These plans have been popular among this age group. Unfortunately, individuals over 26 years of age must purchase coverage that meets minimum creditable coverage, which may be too expensive for many people, particularly those close to the cut-off for subsidies.

While not directly impacted by the reform, individuals of all income levels with access to employer-sponsored insurance experienced increases in their premiums and cost sharing post-reform. Figure 10 shows average employer contributions towards individual premiums pre- and post-reform while Figure11 shows the overall cost of premiums for an individual plan.

An average of a 5 percent drop in employer subsidy towards individual and family premiums(not shown) meant increases in monthly costs for individuals, but it has been at a decreasing rate (Figure 12). In addition to increases in premium costs, employees also faced increases in cost sharing for most services, as shown in Table 1. It is hard to draw a direct correlation with these premium increases and the reform law, as other states saw premiums increase at a faster

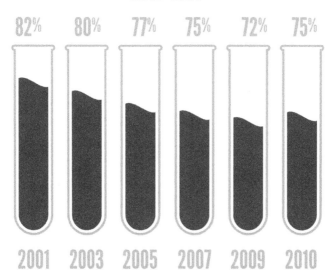

Fig. 10 AVERAGE ANNUAL **EMPLOYER CONTRIBUTION** *in* **MASSACHUSETTS** TOWARDS AN **INDIVIDUAL PLAN** *2001–2010*

82% 80% 77% 75% 72% 75%

2001 2003 2005 2007 2009 2010

Source: DHCFP, Massachusetts Employer Survey. 2001, 2003, 2005, 2007. Center for Survey Research. 2009, 2010

Fig. 11

AVERAGE INDIVIDUAL PREMIUMS
in
MASSACHUSETTS EMPLOYER MARKET
per month

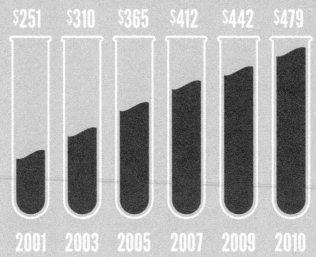

$251	$310	$365	$412	$442	$479
2001	2003	2005	2007	2009	2010

Source: DHCFP, Massachusetts Employer Survey. 2001, 2003, 2005, 2007. Center for Survey Research. 2009, 2010

Fig. 12

MEDIAN EMPLOYEE CONTRIBUTION
for INDIVIDUAL PLANS

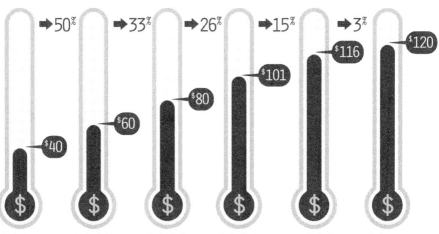

➡ 50%   ➡ 33%   ➡ 26%   ➡ 15%   ➡ 3%

$120
$116
$101
$80
$60
$40

2001   2003   2005   2007   2009   2010

Note: Calculations are based on the median monthly plan premium.
Source: DHCFP, Massachusetts Employer Survey. 2001, 2003, 2005, 2007. Center for Survey Research. 2009, 2010

Table 1

AVERAGE COPAYMENT

	2001	2003	2005	2007	2009	2010
PHYSICIAN OFFICE VISIT	$10	$15	$15	$15	$20	$20
EMERGENCY ROOM	$30	$50	$50	$50	$75	$100
INPATIENT HOSPITALIZATION	–	$50	$250	$250	$250	$300
OUTPATIENT MENTAL HEALTH	–	$15	$15	$20	$20	$20
TIER 1 DRUGS	$8	$10	$10	$10	$10	$15
TIER 2 DRUGS	$15	$20	$25	$25	$25	$30
TIER 3 DRUGS	$25	$35	$40	$45	$45	$50

Source: DHCFP, Massachusetts Employer Survey 2010. July 2011.

rate during the same time period when compared to Massachusetts (not shown). For national context, Figure 13 shows that employer premiums as a percent of median household income for the under-65 population places Massachusetts in the bottom quartile.[8] In other words, while health insurance remains expensive in Massachusetts, higher incomes in the state have kept the percentage of household income spend on insurance at a lower level than in most other states.

Costs – To Employers

Health care reform did little to constrain rapidly rising health care costs and insurance premiums. Small employers, in particular, have been hard hit and have found themselves facing the difficult decision of whether and how to continue their sponsorship of employee health benefits.

The reform added costs to the employer community. There was an increase in demand for insurance under the individual mandate. Employers saw an increase in take-up of coverage along with the continuing annual increases in

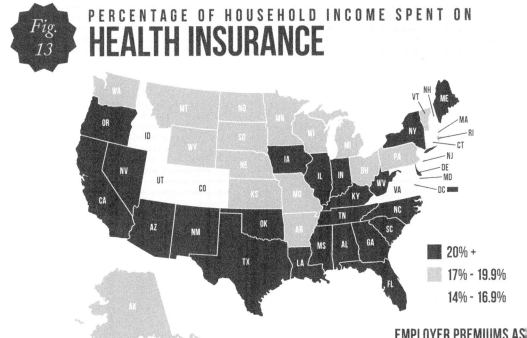

Fig. 13

PERCENTAGE OF HOUSEHOLD INCOME SPENT ON
HEALTH INSURANCE

- 20% +
- 17% - 19.9%
- 14% - 16.9%

EMPLOYER PREMIUMS AS PERCENTAGE OF MEDIAN HOUSEHOL INCOME FOR UNDER-65 POPULATI costs, and employers responded by shifting more of the premium costs onto their employees and increasing cost sharing (Table 1). Some larger employers responded by removing themselves from the fully-insured market and becoming self-insured, as shown in Figure 14, possibly to avoid state mandates.

For smaller, fully-insured employers, there was an increase in the cost of coverage through the Connector's definition of creditable coverage. In addition, there is the cost of eight new mandated benefits passed by the legislature since the reform was enacted. Also, the small group market's health risk was merged with the more volatile, sicker non-group market. Governor Romney had envisioned a new model for small employers that included a defined contribution financing system with greater cost predictability for small employers. However, this model was never implemented by the Connector.

Costs - To Government

Since the reform was implemented, many of the newly insured were insured

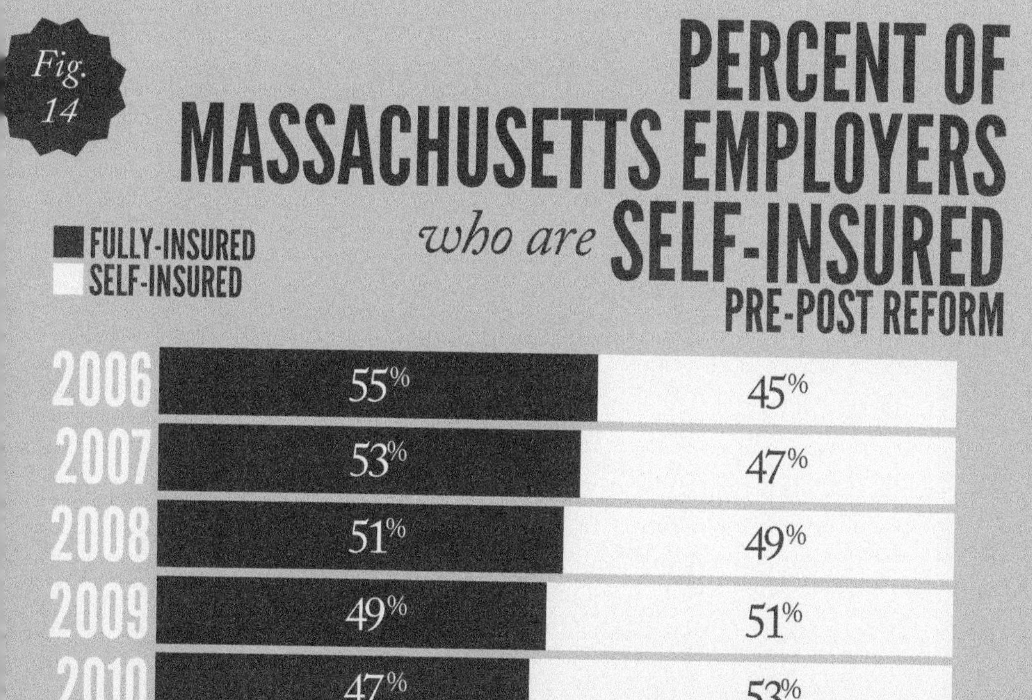

Fig. 14

PERCENT OF MASSACHUSETTS EMPLOYERS *who are* SELF-INSURED
PRE-POST REFORM

- FULLY-INSURED
- SELF-INSURED

Year	Fully-Insured	Self-Insured
2006	55%	45%
2007	53%	47%
2008	51%	49%
2009	49%	51%
2010	47%	53%

rce: UBERP, Health Care in Massachusetts: Key Indicators, May 2011.
e: Self-insured products are arrangements in which an employer provides health benefits to employees and assumes the insurance risk for claims payment. For fully insured panies, the health plan acts as a third party administrator and bears the risk for much of costs. The Employee Retirement Income Security Act (ERISA) exempts self-insured rities from most state oversight, regulations, and mandates.

Fig. 15

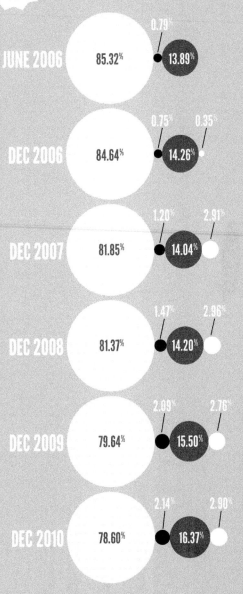

JUNE 2006 — 85.32% | 0.79% | 13.89%
DEC 2006 — 84.64% | 0.75% | 14.26% | 0.35%
DEC 2007 — 81.85% | 1.20% | 14.04% | 2.91%
DEC 2008 — 81.37% | 1.47% | 14.20% | 2.96%
DEC 2009 — 79.64% | 2.09% | 15.50% | 2.76%
DEC 2010 — 78.60% | 2.14% | 16.37% | 2.90%

INSURED POPULATION *by* INSURANCE TYPE

(excludes Medicare enrollees)

- ● PRIVATE GROUP
- ● INDIVIDUAL PURCHASE
- ● MASSHEALTH (MEDICAID)
- ○ COMMONWEALTH CARE

Source: DHCFP, Health Care in Massachusetts: Key Indicators, May 2011 Edition.

	JUN 2006	DEC 2006	DEC 2007	DEC 2008	DEC 2009	DEC 2010	CHANGE
Private Group	4,333,014	4,395,136	4,457,157	4,474,466	4,358,867	4,315,040	-17,974
Individual Purchase	40,184	38,718	65,465	81,073	114,668	117,514	+77,330
MassHealth	705,179	740,563	764,559	780,727	848,528	898,572	+193,393
Commonwealth Care	0	18,327	158,194	162,725	150,998	158,973	+158,973
TOTAL MEMBERS	5,078,377	5,192,814	5,445,375	5,498,991	5,473,061	5,490,099	+441,722

Fig. 16

DRIVERS
in
MASSHEALTH (MEDICAID) ENROLLMENT
2006 - 2010

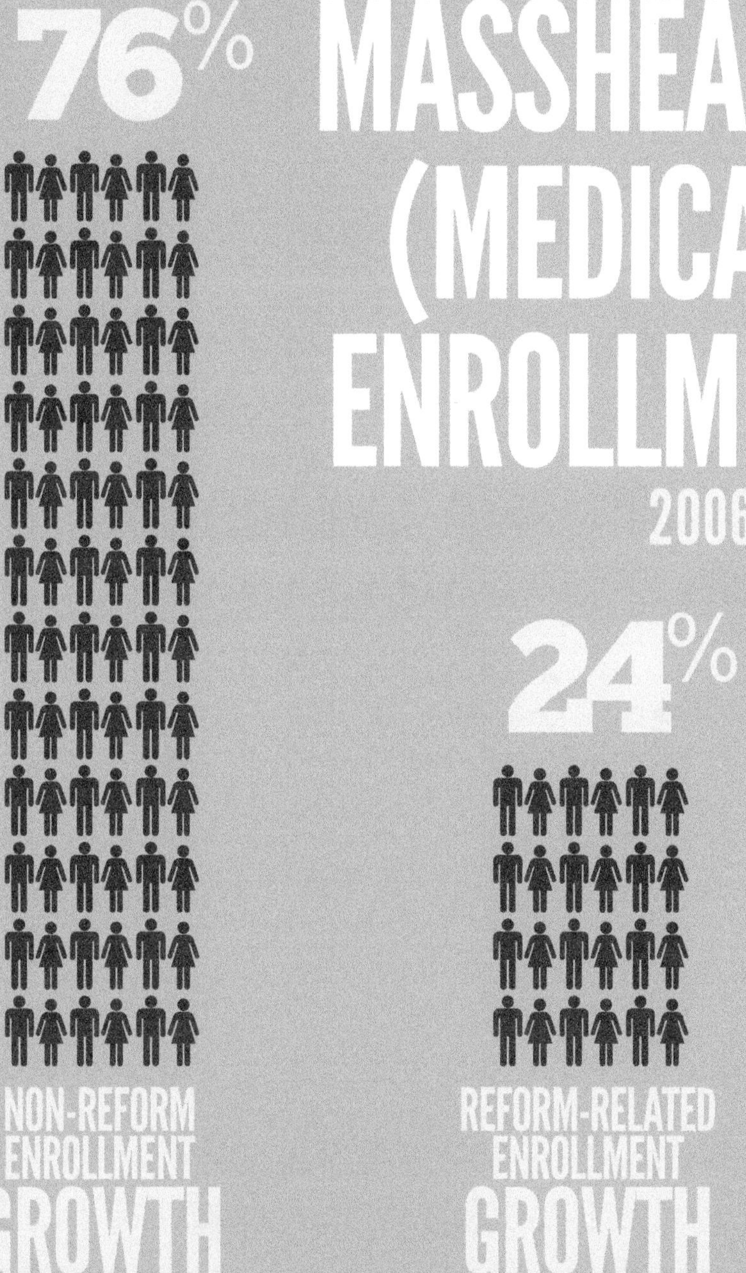

76%

NON-REFORM ENROLLMENT GROWTH

24%

REFORM-RELATED ENROLLMENT GROWTH

Source: Massachusetts Medicaid Policy Institute. MassHealth Enrollment Growth Since Reform. May 2011.

under already-existing or new governmental programs. Figure 15 illustrates the increase in public versus private coverage. Although initially many newly-insured were covered by private insurance, as the recession progressed, the gains in private coverage completely eroded, and most of the newly-insured are now covered by public or publically subsidized insurance. It is important to note, however, that much of the enrollment growth in Medicaid (76%) would have likely occurred without the reform, as is shown in Figure 16. Many other states have seen significant enrollment growth in Medicaid during this same time period.

Many of the costs have been borne by the federal government, as it agreed to provide matching funds to Massachusetts for its reform (via Massachusetts' waiver) and enhanced federal medical assistance percentages (FMAP) that were available to all states in fiscal years 2009, 2010, and part of 2011. Overall spending on the newly-insured population grew from $656 million in state fiscal year 2006 to $1.965 billion in state fiscal year 2010, as shown in Figure 17. Though state spending only increased from $33 million in 2006 to $276 million in 2010 due to the availability of federal funds.

Summary of Cost Results

The cost of health care in Massachusetts has been a problem for a long time. The reform was helpful to some lower-income people who did not have access to affordable insurance. Conversely, most individuals, employers, and the government did not experience any cost savings since the reform was implemented. Massachusetts' policymakers are currently considering various changes to the payment system, although it is uncertain whether any significant reforms will be passed in the near future. Furthermore, it is unclear whether these proposed reforms will have a dampening effect on overall health care costs.

Quality

The last area to examine is the impact of the reform on the quality of care in Massachusetts. Massachusetts has typically scored well on quality

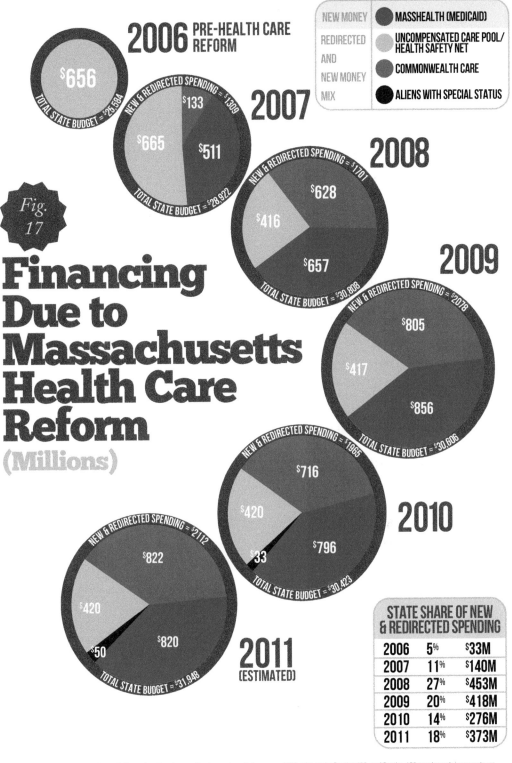

Financing Due to Massachusetts Health Care Reform

(Millions)

Fig. 17

2006 PRE-HEALTH CARE REFORM

NEW MONEY
REDIRECTED
AND
NEW MONEY
MIX

- ● MASSHEALTH (MEDICAID)
- ○ UNCOMPENSATED CARE POOL/ HEALTH SAFETY NET
- ● COMMONWEALTH CARE
- ● ALIENS WITH SPECIAL STATUS

2006
$656
TOTAL STATE BUDGET = $25,584

2007
NEW & REDIRECTED SPENDING = $1309
$133
$665
$511
TOTAL STATE BUDGET = $28,922

2008
NEW & REDIRECTED SPENDING = $1701
$628
$416
$657
TOTAL STATE BUDGET = $30,808

2009
NEW & REDIRECTED SPENDING = $2078
$805
$417
$856
TOTAL STATE BUDGET = $30,606

2010
NEW & REDIRECTED SPENDING = $1965
$716
$420
$33
$796
TOTAL STATE BUDGET = $30,423

2011
(ESTIMATED)
NEW & REDIRECTED SPENDING = $2112
$822
$420
$50
$820
TOTAL STATE BUDGET = $31,948

STATE SHARE OF NEW & REDIRECTED SPENDING		
2006	5%	$33M
2007	11%	$140M
2008	27%	$453M
2009	20%	$418M
2010	14%	$276M
2011	18%	$373M

Note: MassHealth spending includes eligibility and service changes, fee-for-service rate increases, MCO rates under Section 122, and Section 122 supplemental payments, or service basis. No enrollment increases besides those that were directly attributable to eligibility changes have been included in this analysis. Analysis does not include supplemental payments to managed care organizations, the non-federal share of which was funded through local revenues. Uncompensated care pool spending includes offsets from the Medical Assistance Trust Fund. Commonwealth Care spending is net of enrollee contributions. Aliens with special status are legal resident immigrants or those with parole status for 5 years or less. Spending calculations do not include additional administrative costs, start-up costs for the Connector ($25m), or enrollment outreach grants (roughly $12m annually, except FY12) that were associated with the reform.

of care indicators compared to the rest of the nation. Before the reform was implemented, Massachusetts was ranked in the top 10 states for 7 out of 15 measures reported by the Agency for Healthcare Research and Quality (AHRQ) in 2006.[9] Moreover, the reform was not focused on improvements in quality of care. However, there were several initiatives in the law that aimed to improve health care quality. In addition to the creation of the Health Care Quality and Cost Council the legislation included:

- Funding to establish an infection control program. The Department of Public Health received funding to establish and implement an infection control program in licensed health care facilities, and
- A pay-for-performance framework for MassHealth (Medicaid) reimbursements.

For assessment of overall quality metrics pre- and post-reform, AHRQ measures are used, as they allow for easy comparison before and after reform and a comparison to the nation as a whole. The federal reports for a particular year use older data; to conduct this assessment the quality report for 2008 (data

Table 2

CHRONIC CARE QUALITY
Measures & Metrics
COMPARED TO ALL STATES

	ABOVE AVERAGE	AVERAGE	BELOW AVERAGE
2010	50%	19%	31%
2009	32%	41%	27%
2008	30%	45%	26%

Chronic Care: Measures that assess how well health care providers monitor and manage patients with incurable conditions so that the patients can live better lives.
Above Average: The State rate on a National Healthcare Quality Report (NHQR) measure is better than the all-State/regional average and is statistically different from the all-State/regional average.
Average: The State rate on an NHQR measure is not statistically different from the all-State/regional average.
Below Average: The State rate on an NHQR measure is worse than the all-State/regional average and is statistically different from the all-State/regional average.
2008 Measures: most data taken 2005-2006. 2009 Measures: most data taken 2006-2007. 2010 Measures: most data taken 2007-2008.

mostly from 2005 and 2006) is used as the basis for pre-reform and 2010 (data mostly from 2007 and 2008) is used for post-reform. Quality of care is assessed in two areas: acute care, and chronic care.

Quality of Chronic Care

Table 2 presents the percent of chronic measures for which Massachusetts performs better, average, or worse than the national average. Pre-reform, Massachusetts scored better than average on 30% and worse than average on 26% of the measures. Post-reform, Massachusetts scored better than average on 50% of the measures and worse than average on 31%. It should be noted that in the chronic disease area, a number of metrics were not available for the post-reform analysis for Massachusetts, so direct comparisons between the two years cannot be made.

Table 3

ACUTE CARE QUALITY
Measures & Metrics
COMPARED TO ALL STATES

	ABOVE AVERAGE	AVERAGE	BELOW AVERAGE
2010	37%	32%	32%
2009	37%	37%	26%
2008	49%	36%	15%

Acute Care: Measures that assess how well health care providers deliver specific services known to cure disease or speed recovery.
Above Average: The State rate on a National Healthcare Quality Report (NHQR) measure is better than the all-State/regional average and is statistically different from the all-State/regional average.
Average: The State rate on an NHQR measure is not statistically different from the all-State/regional average.
Below Average: The State rate on an NHQR measure is worse than the all-State/regional average and is statistically different from the all-State/regional average.
2008 Measures: most data taken 2005-2006. 2009 Measures: most data taken 2006-2007. 2010 Measures: most data taken 2007-2008.

Quality of Acute Care

Table 3 presents the percent of acute measures for which Massachusetts performs better, average, or worse than the national average. Pre-reform, Massachusetts scored better than average on nearly half and worse than average on just 15% of the acute measures. Post-reform shows some decline in Massachusetts' performance. Massachusetts scored better than average on 37% and worse than average on 32% of the acute care measures.

Summary of Quality Results

The quality of health care in Massachusetts continues to outperform that of other states and national averages on a number of measures. Although the data show that Massachusetts' performance on some of the acute care measures has worsened since the reform, it is difficult to attribute either declines or improvements in quality of care to the reform. More information is needed before a full assessment of the reform's impact on quality of care can be made.

Conclusion

Overall, the outcomes for Massachusetts' reform are varied. Massachusetts embarked on a targeted state experiment that had never been tried before and implementation decisions have come to define where the state stands today. Massachusetts was successful at increasing access to insurance through its combination of mandates and subsidies. Less clear is whether these gains in coverage are sustainable in the long term and whether this access to insurance has translated to access to appropriate care.

Insuring more people had an immediate impact on reducing uncompensated care, but over the duration of the reform this effect has dampened. Massachusetts was less successful in the area of reducing or constraining health care costs for individuals, employers, or government.

Improving quality was not a major aspect of the reform; however, it will be important to monitor whether overall quality improves or deteriorates in the future. The comparisons provided by AHRQ use somewhat older data so it could be useful to continue to monitor trends in quality of care as newer data become available.

8

Lessons and Limitations of Health Insurance Exchanges

Amy Lischko

Health insurance exchanges ("exchanges") entered the national lexicon with the enactment of the Patient Protection and Affordable Care Act (PPACA) in March 2010.[1] The PPACA calls for state-run exchanges that comply with federal rules and guidelines, with a federally-run "fallback" exchange or hybrid federal-state exchange for states that are unwilling or unable to establish their own.

At its most basic level, an exchange is an administrative market-organizing entity with a mission to offer consumers a variety of health insurance plans from which to choose. Proponents believe that exchanges can encourage price competition, increase the portability of health insurance coverage, and provide information to help consumers better understand the options available to them. Critics believe the potential benefits of an exchange have been overstated, and in some instances can be harmful to a market. Health insurance exchanges currently exist in both the public and private sectors.

Questions Abound on the Federal Government's Role

At the time of this writing, numerous questions remain unanswered about the role the federal government will ultimately play in exchanges. In many cases, the PPACA mandates that the U.S. Secretary of Health and Human Services

(HHS) play a broad role in exchange design, approval, and implementation. Yet the complexity of the law and lack of clear comprehensive guidance from the federal government have left states asking basic questions:

- What exchange models will the Secretary of Health and Human Services approve?
- What is the regulatory threshold that HHS will place on the insurance options that must be offered within an exchange?
- What potential role will the Office of Personnel Management-sponsored national health plans or congressionally authorized co-op nonprofit plan play in local markets?
- How will HHS wield its broad waiver authority under PPACA, in areas ranging from approval of Vermont's proposed single-payer system to the granting of medical loss ratio exemptions for insurers serving rural areas?

What We Do Know About PPACA Exchanges?

We know that the PPACA outlines two kinds of exchanges: the American Health Benefit Exchange (AHBE) for individual consumers and Small Business Health Options Program (SHOP) for small employers.[2] The law specifies a number of requirements for an AHBE exchange, but fails to offer an outline for the SHOP exchanges, resulting in uncertainty for many state officials.

The PPACA grants the HHS Secretary broad authority to issue rules and set standards governing the creation and operation of exchanges.[3] State exchanges cannot conflict with federal regulations or standards, but the PPACA outlines a waiver process.[4]

The law also authorizes the HHS Secretary to award grants to state officials in order to set up an AHBE exchange.[5] States can use the money to participate in a multi-state exchange or establish a second focused SHOP. States are required to set up a small business exchange, but can decide if it is part of an AHBE exchange or a separate entity.

The Secretary of HHS has the authority to implement and run a federal fallback exchange in states that decide against (or are deemed incapable of) setting up an exchange on their own by January 1, 2014.[6] Recently, the Centers for Medicare & Medicaid Services (CMS) released rules describing a hybrid exchange (also referred to as a partnership exchange) whereby the state assumes some of the exchange functions.

The law describes exchanges, subject to the Secretary's discretion that, at minimum:

- Certify health plans to be offered in the exchange as "qualified plans"
- Set marketing rules for health plans
- Require insurance plans to have a sufficient number of providers to serve low-income persons
- Verify that health plans meet federally approved quality standards
- Implement a health plan "quality improvement" strategy as defined by federal officials
- Use a "uniform enrollment form" for qualified individuals and employers
- Use a standard format for the presentation of health benefit and plan options
- Provide appropriate information to the exchange's enrollees or prospective enrollees
- Develop a rating system based on quality and price for health plans
- Develop a consumer satisfaction survey to determine the "level of patient satisfaction" with health plans offered through the exchange
- Prepare a template for Internet use for plan comparisons and federal subsidies for coverage, and
- Provide "open enrollment procedures" in accordance with the Secretary's determinations[7]

AHBE exchanges can be run by a government agency or a non-profit entity. Federal law requires state officials to restrict an exchange's health plan offerings to those deemed "qualified," and cover essential health benefits whose standards have been laid out in a recent HHS informational bulletin. At additional cost, states can require a higher level of benefits than those deemed "essential" by the

Secretary of HHS but may not permit plans with fewer mandates. Opponents of the PPACA have expressed concern about this provision for two reasons: they fear that it may lead to unanticipated disruptions to existing state health insurance markets and that it may encourage states to limit consumer options in the insurance market. Critics have also expressed concerns that the exchanges envisioned under the PPACA will simply serve as a "mechanism to expand enrollment in public programs—like Medicaid and the Children's Health Insurance Program (CHIP)—to administer the costly new taxpayer subsidy program and to standardize and regulate consumer choice of private health insurance."[8]

Moving Towards Consumer-Driven Health Care in Exchanges

Market advocates would like to see exchanges serve as passive clearinghouses in order to facilitate a robust defined contribution financing system. In a defined contribution model, an employer gives each employee a fixed dollar amount to purchase insurance rather than paying the cost of providing specified benefits (a "defined benefit model"). This strategy has become widespread in the area of retirement benefits, causing employees to move from classic benefit-defined pensions to 401(k) contributions.[9] Yet in health care, defined contribution models have remained largely underutilized except at larger companies.

Under such an arrangement, employees have a financial incentive to "comparison shop" and balance cost with other considerations. There are explicit incentives for employees to choose the lower cost plans since they are exposed to the difference in premiums for more expensive plans. By introducing market forces into the health insurance purchasing process, it is expected that beneficiaries would become more price-sensitive, and plans would introduce mechanisms to reduce unnecessary utilization and, ultimately, overall health care spending. For employers, fixing a dollar amount to contribute each year for health insurance becomes a predictable expense, with increases directly controlled by the employer.

Under a defined contribution system outside of an employer setting, individuals choose from all available products and benefit designs to purchase a plan that best suits them and their families. Individuals select a plan from a variety of private options and could maintain ownership of such a plan regardless of employment status. Decoupling health insurance from employer sponsorship removes many of the unintended incentives that currently exist in the employer-based insurance system. A defined contribution system could create new incentives for insurers and medical providers to compete for patients and promote experimentation in health plan design and benefits.

Advocates of defined contribution plans believe that this health benefit model would encourage transparency in the current health system, as consumers with more "skin in the game" will demand information on cost, quality and outcomes.[10] It could also drive the development of more creative and flexible plans by insurers seeking to maintain and grow market share. Additionally, as the marketplace moves from group to individual insurance (via individually held employer-supported defined contribution plans), providers will face increasing pressure to be more efficient and to improve the access and convenience of health information and services.[11] Defined contribution plans also offer employers facing difficult economic circumstances the opportunity to continue to offer health benefits.[12] Moreover, this approach removes business owners from decisions related to their employees' health insurance.

Health insurance exchanges can facilitate the implementation of patient-centered and market-based health reforms that expand choice and add value for consumers. However, the exchanges outlined in the PPACA and now taking shape in HHS proposed regulations may have the opposite effect. State officials face a difficult choice—they can, with limited input, implement an ambiguously defined, federally-mandated vision of health reform that may be ill-suited for their insurance market, or they can wait for the federal government to implement its own version with little to no guidance from the states. A state-based option may offer states some control of reform, but with an unknown future cost impact.

A federal fallback or hybrid exchange raises the possibility of U.S. HHS, or a

HHS-designated organization, controlling access to a state's Medicaid program. The PPACA requires that the system being utilized (state-based or federal fallback) determines income eligibility for an exchange, and automatically enrolls Medicaid-eligible individuals in a state's program in order to prevent those individuals from collecting the new federal subsidy.[13] States are restricted from any further eligibility determinations.[14] As a result, the administrator of the exchange controls access to the new federal subsidy as well as the Medicaid program.[15] As they weigh the pros and cons of passing local reforms, states must keep in mind the possibility of a gradual loss of control over their own Medicaid program.

State policymakers should adopt reforms mindful of local market conditions and create mechanisms to maintain control of their Medicaid programs. Market reforms should be targeted at the majority of the uninsured population in each state, informed by the current regulatory environment and the current health infrastructure conditions. The reforms should be sensitive to the level of public and other stakeholder support, and influenced by the current mix of public and private financing. These market-based reforms can lead to meaningful and needed reforms regardless of the ultimate fate of the PPACA.

Lessons on Exchanges from Utah and Massachusetts

Policymakers in many states are facing a difficult decision whether to set up an exchange. The experience of two different states, Massachusetts and Utah, which established their own exchanges pre-PPACA, offer valuable lessons for other states.

Creation of Exchanges

Massachusetts' Commonwealth Health Insurance Connector Authority (Connector) was created by Chapter 58 of the Acts of 2006 as an independent quasi-governmental agency to implement key elements of the Massachusetts health reform law. The Connector manages both a state-subsidized insurance program, "Commonwealth Care," and an unsubsidized insurance program,

"Commonwealth Choice." The Connector was designed to assist both individuals and businesses to acquire health care coverage through these programs; it also assumed numerous policy, administrative, and educational roles to facilitate effective implementation and execution of the overall health reform law. Some states may want to consider the merits of a hybrid exchange as an alternative to either a fully state or federal-based exchange.

The Utah Health Insurance Exchange (UHIE) was established in March 2009 by HB 133 and HB 188. The laws directed the state's Office of Consumer Health Services to develop an internet-based information portal to connect consumers to information they need to make informed choices about health insurance. The overall goal of Utah's exchange is "to serve as the technology backbone to enable the implementation of consumer-based health system reforms."[16] Small employers may offer "defined contribution" benefit plans through the exchange, reducing their administrative burden and making their annual cost for providing insurance more predictable. On the consumer side, the exchange serves three core functions: 1) provide consumers with helpful information about their health care and health care financing; 2) provide a mechanism for consumers to compare and choose a health insurance policy that meets their families' needs; and 3) provide a standardized electronic application and enrollment system.

Policy Considerations for an Exchange

Massachusetts and Utah present at least six lessons for other states considering setting up an exchange. Yet, allowing true flexibility in state execution of local health care reform will result in very different policy solutions. States should have the authority to design and lead their own reforms.

Lesson #1: Where an exchange is housed, and under whose direct authority, will play a large role in shaping the culture, practice, and effectiveness of the organization.

Utah and Massachusetts offer two distinctly different models for exchange governance, oversight, and primary target populations. The UHIE operates with a handful of employees within the Governor's Office of Economic Development, whose mission is to promote the growth of Utah's small business community. This governance configuration has informed many of the operational choices that have been instituted in Utah. The eligibility standards for the Utah exchange initially included the phasing in of small businesses (2-50 employees) and their employees over the first two years. Utah planned to add larger companies in the fall of 2011 but has put that initiative on indefinite hold while UHIE decision-makers try to understand the full impact of the PPACA on their exchange.

The small size of the UHIE staff dictates that much of the operational work of the exchange is done by private entities. Upon its creation, contracts for the system's administrative and financial operation were negotiated quickly, with one-year renewal options to allow for flexibility and modification in vendors and services. Utah's approach in developing its portal was to build on existing technology and work with the existing entities in the health care system to improve the technological interface with consumers.

Utah has developed a cooperative relationship with the business community and relies on significant, unpaid marketing and policy guidance from the private sector. The exchange does not have a board of directors, although it convenes business leaders, primarily through the Salt Lake Chamber of Commerce, to solicit input and advice on its operations. For outreach and education, the entire marketing budget for the exchange is around $10,000 a year, with larger expenditures possible in future years. The exchange has relied on brokers and business organizations to promote its use (99 percent of its business groups in the exchange work with a broker). Despite its meager budget and the lack of an individual or employer mandate in the market, demand for participation in the exchange's launch was enough to quickly fill the 100 available employer slots. A number of the original businesses did not complete the full pilot period, but an expansion in January 2011 resulted in 182 employers and 4,623 covered lives buying through the exchange as of October 2011.[17] The Utah pilot program resulted in some unexpected pricing outcomes, and the legislature made a number of policy changes to address the rating rules.[18] Time will tell if companies see added value in the Utah exchange.

Massachusetts' Connector was established as an independent, quasi-governmental entity that is self-governing, with oversight by a 10-member board of directors under the direction of the state Secretary of Administration and Finance, a cabinet-level appointee of the governor. The board gained an 11th member this summer, as the Legislature added a broker onto the board. The board approves most policy, regulatory and programmatic decisions at the discretion of the executive director, and generally meets on a monthly basis in a public forum. Massachusetts legislators invested significant decision-making authority in the Connector, which has performed many of the regulatory and implementation duties for health reform in the Commonwealth, partly through contracts with other state agencies and private businesses.

But creating an entirely new organization to operate an exchange comes at a cost. The Connector's budget is over $30 million a year and employs about 45 people. Contrast this with Utah's exchange, which employs a handful of employees and costs around $475,000 a year.[19] Overall, the relatively "hands off" approach of the state's legislative and executive branch during the implementation of health care reform has empowered the Connector to act quickly and decisively. Nonetheless, it has concentrated major, system-altering decisions in the hands of a small number of individuals.

One of the fundamental decisions involved in establishing a public exchange is whether it will be under the authority or influence of the state's health care or insurance agency. In Massachusetts, because of the central role that the Connector plays in implementing the health care reform that created it, the state's Division of Insurance ceded responsibility for many policy decisions to the new entity. The program is tethered closely to MassHealth, the state's Medicaid program. MassHealth provides eligibility determination services for the Commonwealth Care program, which is similar in design to Medicaid, and during the early phase of reform relied exclusively on the Medicaid Managed Care Organizations (MMCOs) that served MassHealth to provide benefits for Commonwealth Care enrollees as well (see below for more details).

This has led to what many perceive as a heavy emphasis on the subsidized

Commonwealth Care program. Although the Connector serves both individuals (unsubsidized non-group purchasers and subsidized low-income residents) and small businesses, the focus has been, by far, on low-income individuals without access to employer-sponsored health insurance who are eligible to enroll in subsidized plans offered through Commonwealth Care. Over 90% of the revenue generated for Connector operations comes from the administrative fee earned by the Connector for administering the Commonwealth Care population. As board meeting minutes recorded since the Connector's inception in 2006 show, the Connector board and staff has spent most of their monthly board meeting time discussing issues related to the subsidized population. In comparison, little time has been spent discussing how to establish Commonwealth Choice plans that add more value for non-subsidized individuals and small employers.

The Connector has been implemented to emphasize an active-purchaser exchange model directed by staff and board members, whose decisions limited competition and consumer choice. Plan design choices have not relied on consumer preferences but more on the inclinations and potential biases of regulators. Political pressure, as well as special interests, has influenced the policy making process to ensure a higher level of basic benefits than most consumers would choose on their own, therefore driving up costs.

As Paul Howard at the Manhattan Institute has written:

> Even the most sophisticated active-purchaser model will be dependent on the consistent ability of a relatively small number of exchange administrators to select plans that reflect the real (and shifting) preferences of consumers; adapt to rapid changes in health-care services and technologies; and incorporate novel network or benefit designs that have the potential to improve health while lowering (or slowing the rate of growth of) health-care costs.[20]

An active-purchaser model runs the risk of not being as innovative, aggressive, or agile as a more consumer-based model that allows individuals to register their preferences with their wallets. Consumers should easily be able to select an insurance plan that fits their preference for the location of care (an open versus limited network of providers), the level of benefit coverage, and weigh the cost implications of lower out-of-pocket costs versus a higher premium. Massachusetts is slowly moving in the direction of improving its purchasing process, but is not as far as some private exchanges in this regard.

Lesson #2: The decision to place a subsidized population into a separate pool at start-up may be more politically acceptable; however, it may also prevent the population from transitioning to the competitive private insurance market and cause unnecessary risk-segmentation.

The PPACA offers states the option to set up a basic health program for those with incomes between 138-200% of the federal poverty level (FPL) instead of enabling those individuals to receive subsidies in the exchange.[21] These low-income individuals are just above Medicaid eligibility. State officials considering this option will want to consider Massachusetts' experience with its Commonwealth Care program.

Massachusetts offers one model for facilitating subsidies and the purchase of insurance for lower-income individuals through an exchange. The primary focus of the Connector has been on the subsidized population, which is grouped into its own risk pool and exists entirely within the Connector. When the health care reform passed in Massachusetts in 2006, leading policy makers in the Commonwealth and Washington wanted the subsidized plans to look more like the private market and less like Medicaid. Therefore, the role of purchaser and insurance distributor for the subsidized product, Commonwealth Care, was located within the Connector rather than in the state's Medicaid program. The Connector's half-decade of experience in administering the program suggests that that is where the private market influence ended.

During negotiation of the health reform bill, the safety net hospitals that served a majority of those receiving free care in the Commonwealth expressed a strong concern that they would lose the foundation of their revenue stream under a new insurance-based model—particularly since it was proposed that much of the state's Disproportionate Share Hospital (DSH) funding would be redirected to pay for Commonwealth Care subsidies. To address this concern, the final legislation granted the state's existing four Medicaid managed care organizations (MMCO's) (two of which were also the largest safety-net providers) the exclusive right to serve this population for three years. A fifth carrier, Centene Corporation, was approved to offer Commonwealth Care coverage in July 2009. Centene was the only new insurer to formally pursue the opportunity when bidding was opened; it currently has 36,000 enrollees.

The state's dominant not-for-profit insurers (e.g., Blue Cross Blue Shield of Massachusetts, Harvard Pilgrim Health Care and Tufts Health Plan) and national for-profit insurers have shown a lack of interest in serving the subsidized population in Massachusetts; this indicates that true competition and market forces have yet to take hold in this segment of the market. Premium increases for Commonwealth Care plans have been kept well below the state average for private insurance coverage. This is primarily a result of the captive nature of the relationship—specifically, the dependence of the predominant Commonwealth Care carriers on various forms of state funding. Many believe that significant cost-shifting is still occurring among the various public programs and from private to public plans. When this factor is coupled with the strong political pushback on rate increases by the Connector board and Massachusetts' governor, one can see why most of the state's major non-profit insurers and national for-profit carriers have shown a reluctance to participate.

This situation could create problems for Commonwealth Care recipients if/when they transition from subsidized care into private coverage. They will not only face the loss of the subsidy, but many will need to move to another carrier and face the relatively higher cost of the private insurance market, which is pooled separately and is not under the same rate negotiations as the Commonwealth Care program.

Lesson #3: System capabilities including IT compatibility and connectivity can limit advances in administrative simplicity and bog down potential innovation.

One of an exchange's primary goals is to transform the purchase of insurance from a confusing web of paperwork to a transaction akin to purchasing an airline ticket online. In order to achieve this goal, all transactions need to be fully integrated and automated to reduce paperwork, improve system and supply chain efficiency, and increase customer satisfaction. That means that brokers, consumers and employers should be able to compare price and quality information across plans and providers, get quotes, conduct cost-benefit analysis across plan types, combine payments from different payers, pay premium, and enroll in a plan, all via an electronic interface.

Technology challenges exist for states interested in facilitating a model that transforms the purchase of health insurance from the employer to the individual. How and with whom the state contracts for these services can make a big difference in the launch and ongoing capabilities of an exchange.

In Utah, three of the largest insurers in the state are currently participating in the new defined contribution market. Other carriers expressed interest in participating in the launch but were unable to because of internal technology challenges. On the web portal side, the exchange has taken a relatively open approach to the addition of services and functions to its site, which has allowed for an expansion of offerings--even in the short period of time for which the site has been operating. The exchange has had its technology challenges including the inability to launch a successful premium aggregator function.

Massachusetts also faced significant technological challenges in both its Commonwealth Care and Commonwealth Choice programs. In fact, to date the two programs remain operationally separated with distinct vendors responsible for enrollment, customer service, quality assurance, and billing.

In order to get systems up and running quickly, the Connector initially made the decision to purchase services for Commonwealth Care from existing Medicaid vendors. Almost immediately there arose a number of billing system challenges, stemming from the fact that Commonwealth Care had a variety of benefit and co-payment structures, which were hard to align with Medicaid's much more standardized billing process. The challenges included the vendor's inability to process accurate monthly premium bills for Commonwealth Care consumers who frequently churn through the system and the renewal process for individuals, which was to many cumbersome and confusing. In addition, the close linkage with the Medicaid program (particularly around eligibility) made it difficult to provide accurate, understandable correspondence to members regarding eligibility and benefits.

Challenges in the Commonwealth Choice program included shortcomings in the initial billing system, which did not allow for e-payment of premiums (an electronic pay system was subsequently set up in Spring 2009). Moreover, no technology currently exists for accepting premium payments from multiple sources, such as two spouses or contributions from multiple employers. The small group employer contributory plan pilot had a very rocky launch due to problems with the program's website and the provision of information to brokers.

Lesson #4: Small businesses are seeking added value through the use of an exchange, including assumption of HR functions, a predictable cost structure (defined-contribution program), and the ability to remove themselves from the insurance plan selection process.

An exchange can operate as a distribution channel for small businesses seeking insurance for their workforce and introduce greater portability, affordability and choice in the small employer insurance marketplace. It can be established as an optional or exclusive distribution channel; Massachusetts and Utah, once again, offer two models for discussion.

The need for increased affordability in the small group market in Massachusetts was acknowledged as an important goal for health reform. Choice and portability were also values that the bill's original architects thought were important. While the Connector began offering a voluntary (non-contributory) insurance program for employees without access to employer-sponsored insurance (ESI) in September 2007, its small employer program did not launch until December 2008, and only on a pilot basis.

The so-called Contributory Plan (CP) allowed small employers with 50 or fewer full-time employees to subsidize their employees' purchase of health insurance. However, the small group contributory plans did not provide for greater predictability for employers, as Massachusetts chose not to include a full-blown defined contribution method. Instead, each employer selected a level of plan for its employees (Gold, Silver or Bronze) and agreed to pay at least 50% towards the employee premium (and meet employer participation rules). Also, a base employer contributory amount was set based on the employer's selection of a plan within a coverage tier. Employees could then take that base employer contribution and select any carrier's plan within the tier of coverage selected by the employer, but they could not buy a product outside the tier that their employer selected. In addition, during the pilot phase, the Connector selected 20 brokers to participate at a reduced fee, and restricted sales to preexisting clients of those brokers.

Even with the lengthy delay in its launch, the CP suffered from design flaws. The program drew limited interest from the small business community and failed to reach its initial goal of 100 employers. The designs of the health insurance products offered through the Connector lacked creativity and were similar to options available outside of the Connector.[22] While plans were required to be rated using a modified community rating system similar to plans outside of the Connector, CP insurers were prohibited from re-rating a plan regardless of the characteristics of the final enrollees. Additionally, for employees choosing to deviate from the employer-selected benchmark plan, a list billing (or age rating) was used, making the switch unattractive to older workers.[23] Moreover, many of the plans lacked network diversity. At the time, the legislature prohibited the Connector from offering mandate-lite (or basic benefit) plans to small businesses, prohibited pooling purchasing groups, and limited the program to employers with 50 or fewer employees. Finally, the Connector narrowly focused its own advertisements to employers not already offering insurance, a small portion of the market. These factors, plus consistent, double-digit increases in annual premiums, have combined to make this aspect of the Connector's mission its least successful.

The Connector froze enrollment in the CP and launched a new small business program called Business Express (BE), "put[ting] its resources into one effort for small businesses."[24] However, Business Express also suffers from design limitations and does little to address the underlying reasons behind premium increases. It reduces the monthly fee that small employers typically pay to third-party administrators from $35 per subscriber to $10 per subscriber, saving employers roughly $300 per employee per year.[25] But this reduced fee is not unique to the Connector. The Massachusetts Business Association contends that it offers a similarly low administrative fee. The results are disappointing, especially given the opportunity that existed in 2006 to transform the small group purchasing experience.

Meanwhile, insurance rates for businesses under 50 employees have increased by double digits in each of the last four years, enough so that Massachusetts Governor Deval Patrick filed legislation to expand the authority of the state's Division of Insurance over health insurance premiums, allowing it to review insurance rates for small businesses before they go into effect and adjusting them if they are deemed "excessive" or "unreasonable." It is clear that health care reform and the Connector's model for small employers has not addressed the central issues of affordability and predictability for small employers.

In contrast, the Utah Exchange's biggest drawing card is that it is the only outlet through which employers can establish and fund a defined contribution plan for their employees. Although any individual is able to use the exchange to compare plans, the system was primarily designed for small employers, allowing for comparison, enrollment, premium determination, billing and collection. Employers determine how much they will contribute toward employees' premiums and then establish accounts for them with the exchange. After collecting limited health histories from all employees, the exchange creates a risk premium for the employer and applies it in determining the individual's final premium. Once this is completed, the employee can choose from the roughly 80 plans that are displayed through the portal.[26] Officials in Utah are still determining whether the state's model will successfully contain health care costs for small employers while providing greater choice and portability for employees.

Lesson #5: An exchange with limited product choice for individuals that exists side-by-side with alternative distribution channels should, at a minimum, develop robust consumer information and administrative support in the area of customer service.

An important question for policymakers, who decide to set up an exchange, is how to position a SHOP exchange within the existing distribution channels in a state. Will it be an alternative to, work closely with, or subsume the current channels?

The Connector has been most successful in enrolling people in products where the statute deemed it to be the exclusive distributor, that is, in the subsidized Commonwealth Care program and the young adult marketplace, where carriers may offer plans with limited benefits to individuals aged 18 to 26. For small employers and non-subsidized adults over the age of 26, it has not made significant progress. Many eligible individuals continue to purchase their insurance outside the Connector.

Since reform began, about half of new enrollees in the non-subsidized, non-group market have purchased their coverage through the Connector. In some cases this is because they require more assistance in purchasing insurance than the Connector's web-based tools allow. Although the Connector has established a customer service center, it relies primarily on a web-based model for shopping and enrolling in coverage. Consumers who need more guidance for their insurance purchase typically call the carriers directly to obtain individualized support and then enroll directly with them.

In addition, there is a wider choice of products for individuals outside the Connector. Some carriers offer products that do not fit into standardized categories that the Connector sets. The Connector developed a "seal of approval" process through which plans offered through the Connector must meet higher standards in terms of benefit levels than some of the plans in place for the state's overall insurance market. Connector staff inclinations and board members' belief that standardization was important prompted the Connector to further reduce the number of options available to consumers, but more recently it has granted insurers greater flexibility in plan design. However, if consumers continue to purchase products offered outside the Connector with greater frequency, the Connector will need to evaluate whether this is a sustainable model.

States considering an exchange as a distribution channel for individuals must have experienced staff who have the necessary IT expertise and understand the commercial health insurance market. These staff are essential for developing decision tools (either internally or with the private sector) that present choices to consumers in a way that is easily understood. Licensed health insurance agents are required to provide excellent real-time customer service to individuals requiring additional support for the entire transaction.

Lesson #6: Broker, provider, and carrier support for reform is essential to success, both in passing exchange legislation and implementing a functional exchange.

One of the lessons learned from earlier versions of small business purchasing cooperatives was the importance of harnessing broker, provider, and carrier support.[27] Other states are advised not to underestimate these key stakeholders. Massachusetts and Utah demonstrate two different approaches.

An important barrier to the Connector's success has been resistance from brokers and carriers. An inability to tap the broker and payer networks more effectively in Massachusetts has resulted in continuing difficulties for the Connector, particularly in the small group market. Brokers make more money from a carrier if they bring an employer to a single carrier versus sharing the administrative fee with the Connector. Brokers also tend to concentrate volume with particular carriers because their commissions increase as a result, and there are significant retention incentives.

Although one could argue that it is less work for the broker to bring the employer to the Connector, as the Connector assumes some administrative responsibilities, thus far that has not been a persuasive argument. Brokers have remarked that it is more work for them to explain to employers how this new model operates. Before passage of the reform law, brokers had saturated Massachusetts' small employer market, creating longstanding, trusted relationships. Brokers are often responsible for the multitude of administrative tasks involved with purchasing insurance coverage, including explaining any changes in state or federal law that apply to employers, processing paperwork, and providing human resources support. It seems likely that the Connector needs to offer improvements in broker connectivity and other incentives in order to become a major player in the distribution of insurance to small employers. The relationship was harmed when the Connector pulled the addresses of small businesses from the Department of Revenue to solicit business directly. In response, brokers pushed the legislature to pass a law to prohibit this practice in the future, and another to add a broker to the Connector board.

Massachusetts carriers also remain skeptical of the Connector and continue to provide and promote direct service to employer groups for administrative and risk selection reasons. The carriers with more market share have the most to lose if the Connector becomes a significant distribution channel for the small employer market. Not only will those dominant carriers give up market share, they will also disrupt broker relationships. Moreover, carriers are understandably risk-averse and are afraid that if employees are given choices, they will segment themselves in a way that will result in adverse selection. Carriers have just started delivering meaningful narrow or limited network plans which are more affordable and more attractive to small employers in an exchange model. Carriers greatly influenced the Connector to begin with a pilot program for its Contributory Plan for small employers, and to allow employee choice only within a tier of coverage.

Without the individual mandate or subsidies provided for in Massachusetts, policymakers in Utah realized that support for the initiative from the state's insurance brokers was a key element to their future success. Exchange staff developed strong relationships with brokers in designing and implementing their reform plan. Early feedback indicated that consistent, ongoing communication with and guidance from brokers, insurers and the business community has contributed to the enthusiastic reception the exchange has received.

The Utah exchange has addressed the risk concerns of carriers head-on by developing a risk-adjustment methodology and implementing the program in a pilot fashion. This has occurred in what is arguably a more complex environment, as Utah allows for rate adjustment for the health of an employer group in Utah while Massachusetts does not.

Tough Choices on Exchanges Ahead for State Officials

State officials face an ambiguous future on exchanges, yet aside from the PPACA, health reform is needed in many states. Policymakers must decide if they will wait for the PPACA to run its judicial and political course before passing local reform, or move now. State reforms can serve as a hedge against future federal intervention, but also can best serve the health insurance needs of the residents of a state.

States that remain on the sidelines must consider the long term implications of inaction on their insurance market and the federal involvement in their Medicaid program. With a lack of clarity surrounding the many and complex exchange provisions of the PPACA, the smartest step forward is for state lawmakers to adopt reforms that position their state for a range of possible outcomes.

The implementation requirements for the PPACA are changing frequently. These and future regulations are likely to change dramatically if there is a switch of political party control in the White House and the Senate in January 2013. While state officials may wish for more clarity from the federal government, it is unlikely to come any time soon. As a result, state officials should pass reforms that contain the disruption of the PPACA and target modifications toward gaps in local insurance markets.

Part 3

An Effective Reform Agenda

Conclusion

A Federal-State Framework for Market-Based Reform

James C. Capretta

Despite criticism from some quarters, the health care system in the United States has significant strengths. The hospitals and clinics through which most Americans get their care are staffed by some of the world's most highly trained and accomplished physicians and these institutions have the capacity to deliver the finest and most sophisticated medical care found anywhere in the world. Most Americans have ready access to this care through third-party insurance arrangements provided by their employers, or in the case of seniors, by Medicare. Finally, U.S. health care is open to medical innovation in ways that other systems around the world are not. The resulting rapid pace of innovation that has occurred in recent decades has, in the main, provided a tremendous boost to the quality of patient care.

There are also many problems with American health care. These problems are aggravated by the Patient Protection and Affordable Care Act (PPACA) but they will remain even if the PPACA is repealed. These problems have worsened in the past three decades, to the point where a large percentage of the electorate believes real change is needed.

These problems include:

- Cost increases that exceed the levels that patients, taxpayers, or other payers are either able or willing to pay

- Government spending on health care that is rising much more rapidly than the revenue base that pays for it, thus putting tremendous strain not just on governmental finances but also on U.S. economy and credit-worthiness
- A substantial number of Americans with pre-existing conditions who either cannot afford or cannot find insurance options that provide secure and sufficient coverage for their conditions
- A considerable number of working Americans who go without insurance for long periods or intermittently because they cannot afford it or it is not offered by their employers
- A surprisingly low and unpredictable quality of care in many settings

What the American health care sector needs most is the discipline, balance, and accountability that come from a functioning marketplace. Normally, competition among suppliers of services and products ensures that consumers get value for the money they spend. It also rewards entrepreneurs who find better ways to provide what consumers want and need. That is not the case with health care in the United States today. Americans looking to purchase affordable coverage face a marketplace distorted by current government policy and misallocated federal and state responsibilities. In a country as large and diverse as the United States , it is impossible to centralize key aspects of decision-making about health care in Washington, D.C. without running roughshod over the prerogatives of state and local officials as well as the rights and freedoms of individual citizens and their families.

Effective reform of American health care must be built on two key principles. First, only a functioning marketplace can impose needed cost discipline without sacrificing what is good and desirable about the quality of American medicine. Second, effective oversight and governance of health policy in the country will only occur in a system that respects federalism.

This chapter serves as a guide for members of Congress and state legislators on how they should, in practice, apply these twin principles. Effective policymaking requires a level of understanding about what is and is not working in current federal and state policy, and also an understanding that neither the federal government nor the states can independently address the problems we face. The only answer to the health care riddle is a healthy, constructive federalism, wherein each level of government plays its proper role.

Distorted Federal and State Roles = Rapid Cost Escalation

The foundational document of our federal system of government enumerates in broad terms the powers to be exercised by the federal and state levels of government in economic matters. The Constitution gives the federal government the authority to regulate interstate commerce on matters which bear on the functioning of the national economy; the states hold authority over all matters not expressly reserved as federal concerns. Our constitutional framework provides the right boundaries for a well-functioning federalist approach to health care governance. The trick is to ensure that authority for political decision-making lies at the proper level of political accountability.

Health care will almost certainly always entail some level of shared oversight by the federal and state governments. On one level, health care is obviously a local economic good. In most instances, patients need the attention and care of trained and competent medical professionals in close proximity to where they live. That quite clearly means that the states will have great interest in overseeing the system of service delivery to ensure it is accessible for their citizens and of high quality.

At the same time, there is clearly a role for the federal government in health care. After all, communicable diseases can travel across state lines, and the free flow of persons and products throughout the country means that some coordination across the states is a legitimate concern of federal officials. Also, with rapid improvements in communications and information technology, more and more services will cross state lines and fall under federal jurisdiction.

Unfortunately, instead of a carefully constructed system of divided responsibility, our system of health care oversight and regulation has grown up on an ad hoc basis, driven mainly by well-intentioned policies at the federal level that were enacted long ago but that now have dramatic unintended consequences.

Through tax and regulatory policies, the federal government has effectively nationalized health insurance oversight for many tens of millions of Americans (and that may be said without taking into account the dramatic centralization that would occur if PPACA is not repealed). This movement of power and control over health insurance to the federal government has occurred even though states have historically been the main regulators of all types of commercial insurance products.

Federal Tax Exemption and ERISA

The interplay of two key provisions of current federal health care law account for the shift in power to the federal government away from states. During World War II, the IRS made a regulatory decision to exempt employer-paid premiums from the federal definition of taxable income during the wartime era's tight wage controls. This significant tax break was codified after the war; it became the impetus for widespread adoption of employer-sponsored health plans in the 1950s and 1960s. Indeed, the principal driver for the U.S. adoption of a system of employer-based health insurance as the primary insurance platform for the working age Americans was federal tax law, which has made such coverage financially advantageous for both employers and employees.

As explained in Tom Miller's chapter *The Case for Competition and Choice through Healthy Federalism*, the federal tax treatment of employer-sponsored coverage provides an incentive for higher levels of spending rather than economizing. Today, employer-paid health insurance premiums do not count as taxable compensation for workers. No matter how expensive the health insurance premium, if the employer is paying, it is tax-free to the worker. Employees thus have a strong incentive to take more and more of their compensation in the form of health coverage instead of cash wages because health coverage is not taxable. For every dollar spent on health coverage, a worker receives a full dollar of coverage; whereas for every dollar received in other forms of compensation, a portion goes to the government in the form of taxes.

Later, Congress enacted the Employee Retirement Income Security Act (ERISA), which regulates employer-sponsored benefit programs. The effect of the ERISA law and subsequent court decisions was to exempt employer-sponsored self-insured[1] health plans from state health insurance regulation. For many employers, that exemption is highly valued: it exempts their health plans from the myriad of benefit mandates that state legislatures across the country have adopted over the years. Importantly, by putting a large slice of the marketplace beyond their policy reach, the ERISA law has made it nearly impossible for states to take the lead in substantial health care reform.

Politically, these alterations to traditional, market-based health care arrangements have proven to be nearly impossible to correct. Americans working for the nation's largest employers have grown accustomed to, and comfortable with, the generous plans they now receive. Their employers do not have to deal with the idiosyncratic requirements of fifty separate insurance regulators. Together, large self-insured firms and their employees have become a powerful force in public debates about health care policy. They strongly resist changes that might disrupt how they go about their business.

Assertions that America's experiment in market-driven health care has failed because of out-of-control cost escalation is a false characterization of the historical development of health care in this country. The U.S. does not have an effective health care marketplace; rather the U.S. has a system that has been distorted by the misaligned incentives embedded in existing federal health care policies. Certainly, the federal tax exemption for employer-paid premiums has distorted the health care marketplace. But equally important distortions have come about from the establishment and expanding presence of federal regulations associated with the Medicare and Medicaid programs.

Medicare and Medicaid

Aside from employer-sponsored coverage, most other Americans are insured through the federal government's giant public insurance programs, Medicare and Medicaid. These programs are highly valued by their enrollees, and for good reason. They are crucial to securing access to care for the nation's senior and low income households. Nonetheless, Medicare and Medicaid also contribute substantially to the problems which plague American health care too. For starters, because of their design, Medicare and Medicaid distort political incentives and accountability. More importantly, they also provide open-ended government subsidies that increase as costs rise. The result is a much-diminished incentive for insistence on high performance, efficiency, and quality in the provision of health care.

Though states retain prerogatives relating to the licensing of health care providers, the federal government has also become the dominant regulator of hospitals, physicians, and other providers of care through the Medicare program. When enacted in 1965, Medicare was supposed to be a third-party insurer with a minimal role in the oversight and regulation of the delivery of health care services. At the time, states had the clear lead in the oversight of medical practice. But Medicare's restrained role was short-lived. Within a few years of enactment, the bureaucracy running the program began to issue rules for the reimbursement of services. Since seniors are the heaviest users of health care services, no provider of medical care can ignore Medicare's regulatory demands. As a result, over the past four decades, hospitals and physicians have organized themselves entirely around Medicare's rules, with virtually no input from state governments.

Medicare's cost impacts are equally clear. Most program beneficiaries sign up with the traditional fee-for-service (FFS) insurance arrangement the program provides. The status quo allows enrollees to see any licensed service provider, with no questions asked. Medicare requires substantial cost sharing—including 20 percent coinsurance to see a physician and a more than $1,000 deductible per hospital admission—but this cost sharing is ineffective because some 90 percent of the enrollees also purchase some form of supplemental coverage, which pays for unreimbursed expenses. Thus, in most instances, Medicare's beneficiaries pay nothing extra when they get more care.

Congress and the Medicare program's administrators have tried to hold down Medicare's costs by paying less for each service provided. Those providing services to Medicare patients have responded over time by providing more services, and more intensive treatment, for the same conditions. In most cases, there is no incentive to opt for lower-volume care. Patients generally do not pay more money out of pocket when more services are rendered, and those providing services generate more income with each additional procedure or test. The bill is simply passed on to the Medicare program — and federal taxpayers.

The result of this dynamic is hardly surprising. The volume of services paid for by Medicare has been on a steady and steep upward trajectory for decades. According to the Congressional Budget Office (CBO), the real price Medicare paid for physician fees dropped between 1997 and 2005 by nearly 5 percent, but total Medicare spending for physician services rose 35 percent because of rising use and more intensive treatment per condition.[2]

Enacted in 1965 at the same time as Medicare, Medicaid, too, is structured in a way that undermines effective health care policy. Medicaid was set up explicitly to be a state-driven program; the program is financed by a system of federal matching payments for state-determined Medicaid spending. The federal share of Medicaid spending varies by state, but on average, federal taxpayers pick up 57 percent of every dollar of Medicaid expenses, and state taxpayers pay the rest.[3]

This approach to financing Medicaid undermines political accountability for budgetary costs. Neither the federal government nor the states are ultimately in charge, nor are they accountable. As one might expect, the federal government has over time imposed tighter and tighter rules on what states can and cannot do with federal Medicaid funding, much to the dismay of state governors and legislators. At the same time, states have sought to maximize federal Medicaid payments to ease their budgetary pressures. Indeed, much state spending, such as public health and mental health funding financed entirely by state taxpayers prior to the establishment of Medicaid, has over the past four decades found its way into the Medicaid budget.

Worse still, the current approach to financing Medicaid undermines political incentives to insist on cost discipline. Governors or state agencies seeking to cut their state's Medicaid costs must cut the program by $2.30 to save $1.00 in state money because the first $1.30 belongs to the federal treasury. Not surprisingly, most state politicians do not find that a particularly appealing formula. So, instead of pursuing difficult and controversial reforms, they spend most of their energy working on ways to maximize federal Medicaid matching payments while simultaneously minimizing state costs.

The results are predictable: Medicaid costs have risen rapidly almost without interruption since the program was enacted, and, yet, there are still millions of low-income Americans who lack insurance.

The Big Picture

When these factors are taken together—Medicare's incentives for rising volume, unlimited federal matching payments for state-run Medicaid plans, and a tax subsidy for employer plans that grows with the expense of the plan—it is no surprise that U.S. health care costs are rising rapidly.

And the distortions do not end there. Because of the design of these subsidy arrangements, the biggest customers in our health system are not patients but the big payers of insurance claims filed by doctors and hospitals— namely, the federal government, the states, and the country's employers. The current payment structure goes a long way toward explaining the uneven quality of American health care. Workers who receive insurance coverage through their employers cannot change their insurance if their current plans require unnecessary and repetitive paperwork, and they have little choice in deciding which doctors and hospitals are covered in their networks. Moreover, doctors and hospitals organize their operations to maximize payments, not to use convenient and consumer-focused care to attract patients. The result is maddening bureaucracy, paperwork, and unaccountable service delivery.

Moreover, the opaque nature of today's taxpayer-supported insurance arrangements makes it difficult to recognize who benefits the most from the current system. In particular, it is not widely understood that the tax preference for employer-paid premiums provides greater value for higher-income households that are in higher-rate tax brackets than for low-wage workers who most need assistance to pay for health coverage. According to Congress's Joint Committee on Taxation, in 2007, the average value of the tax preference for job-based coverage was about $2,000 for households with incomes between $10,000 and $30,000 per year and $4,600 for households with incomes between $200,000 and $500,000 per year.[4] Higher-salaried workers have the strongest incentive to consume the most expensive insurance.

Federal support for health insurance coverage through entitlements and the federal tax break for job-based plans help explain why the federal budget today is in deep deficit, and why the long-term outlook is daunting. According to the Congressional Budget Office (CBO), the federal government will run a cumulative budget deficit of $4.8 trillion over the period 2011 to 2021, following a two-year deficit of $2.7 trillion in 2009 and 2010.[5] And those projections assume that a $4 trillion tax increase will be imposed beginning in 2013. A realistic set of policy assumptions shows federal debt headed toward 100 percent of GDP.[6]

A major reason for all of this red ink – indeed, the most important reason – is runaway health costs, as reflected in federal spending on Medicare and Medicaid as well as the tax break for job-based coverage. According to the CBO, combined Medicare and Medicaid spending will reach $1.5 trillion in 2021, nearly double the spending in 2010.[7] Over the next 25 years, the CBO expects federal spending on the major health entitlements to rise from about 5.5 percent to 10.3 percent of GDP.[8]

Market-Driven Health Care vs. Government-Imposed Cost Controls

Debates over health care policy tend to be polarized, with a deep divide over what needs to be done to slow the pace of rising costs. On one side are the governmentalists who believe that central government management of prices and government reengineering of service delivery by doctors and hospitals can control costs without affecting the quality of care. This mindset has dominated health policymaking at the federal level, most especially in the context of the Medicare program, for the better part of a half century. It has not worked.

It has not worked because the government does not have the capacity to make the difficult decisions required to build a high-value network of care provision. The private sector delivery models that are admired by the experts — like Geisinger Health System (Pennsylvania), the Cleveland Clinic (Ohio), and Intermountain Healthcare (Utah) — operate on a principle of provider exclusivity. They operate highly selective, if not totally closed, networks, that enable these providers to gain control over the delivery system. They drop or avoid low-quality performers, and establish tight processes to streamline care and eliminate unnecessary steps.

Despite years of demonstration projects and multiple initiatives, the federal government has not shown itself capable of building anything remotely similar to these models for the public insurance programs. When attempts have been made in the past to steer patients toward preferred physicians or hospitals, they have failed because politicians and regulators find it impossible to make distinctions among hospitals and physician groups based on disputable quality measures.

Instead, Congress and Medicare's regulators have cut costs through across-the-board payment rate reductions that apply to every licensed provider without regard to measures of quality or efficient performance. It is notable that despite all of the talk of "delivery system reform" in the PPACA, the way the new law cuts Medicare spending is with old-fashioned payment rate reductions, not new approaches to delivering care.

The alternative to the failed, top-down approach of government micromanagement is a functioning marketplace. The key to building such a marketplace is cost-conscious consumers.[9] Instead of a defined benefit entitlement, participants in a defined contribution system get a fixed-dollar payment from the government; they can use this payment to purchase an insurance plan of their own choice. If they select expensive coverage, they pay the difference out of their own resources. If they choose less expensive plans, they pay lower premiums and keep the savings. This structure provides a powerful incentive for health system participants to find high-value plans that charge low premiums.

Critics argue that this type of reform will not control health care costs, and will only shift the burden and risk of rapidly rising costs onto individuals and away from the government. This way of looking at the impact and reach of a defined contribution reform represents a distinct case of tunnel vision. In a defined contribution system in which cost-conscious consumers seek out the best value for their money, cost-cutting innovations would be rewarded, not punished, as they are today. Physicians and hospitals would have strong financial incentives to reorganize themselves to increase productivity and efficiency to capture a larger share of what would become a highly competitive marketplace. *This is the only way to slow the growth of health-care costs without lowering the quality of care.*

Medicare Part D, the prescription drug benefit, which was enacted in 2003 and fully implemented by 2006, provides strong evidence of the value of approaches that draw on competition and consumer choice to control the growth of health care costs.

The Part D drug benefit was designed to harness the power of consumers looking for value. The new drug benefit requires no government-sponsored plan or option; instead, it is delivered entirely through private insurance plans that submit bids to the federal government. These bids are based on the premium amounts that insurers charge for providing drug coverage. The government then calculates, based on a weighted average of those bids, what it will pay on a regional basis. Importantly, the government's contributions do not vary depending on the plans selected by the beneficiaries. In essence, the government's contribution toward drug coverage becomes a defined contribution payment on behalf of Medicare beneficiaries. If a beneficiary selects a plan that costs more than the Medicare contribution, he or she pays the difference out of pocket. Conversely, selection of a relatively less expensive plan reduces the enrollee's out-of-pocket premium payments.

When it was enacted, the competitive drug benefit design had numerous critics.[10] Some argued that the program would not work because private plans would decline to participate without a guaranteed share of the market. Others said the beneficiaries would not sign up for it because the competitive structure was too complex to navigate. Others said program costs would explode without government-regulated price controls.

All of these predictions proved to be wrong. Now in its sixth year of implementation, the program has exceeded all expectations. Some 90 percent of Medicare participants are in secure drug coverage of some sort, and public opinion surveys show that they are very satisfied with their insurance.[11] Most importantly, the program is coming in significantly under budget, with costs over the first decade running 42 percent below estimates at the time of its enactment.[12]

The Road Ahead to a Functioning Health Care Market

Diagnosing the problems in American health care, and with the approach taken in the PPACA, is not enough. It is crucial also to build a framework within which a functioning marketplace can deliver higher value, lower cost care. Doing so requires addressing several key questions:

- What level of government should address various actions that will move market reforms ahead?
- What strategy should elected leaders employ to remove federally created distortions to the health care market?
- How should we incorporate market-based reform with respect to issues like coverage for pre-existing conditions?
- How can federal and state governments help solve the Medicaid puzzle?

The final section of this chapter provides answers to these important questions.

State Administration of a Market-Based Reform

There are two temptations that must be resisted with regard to a market-based health care reform. The first is the temptation to federalize every decision. If current law and PPACA have tended toward centralization in the name of increasing governmental control, reformers with a market-based orientation might be tempted to go in the other direction and impose their vision of a functioning marketplace with federal law and no room for states to play a role on behalf of their citizens. This would also be an error, and shortsighted. If the federal government makes all the decisions, the tendency of distant bureaucracies to build power and ignore the concerns of dissenting voices will eventually lead to even greater government controls than those that are present in today's system. Undoubtedly, the best protection against the federal government's tendency to overextend its reach is to have states serve as the main administrators of a market-based system.

The other temptation is to move too quickly, in the name of reform, to upend existing arrangements that have been built around the rules currently in place. This is a particular concern for the health insurance plans now sponsored by large employers for millions of American workers. Indeed, the fear that PPACA will impose unnecessary costs on these plans is a significant cause of the law's unpopularity among a sizeable plurality of the electorate.

A well-crafted reform must steer clear of both temptations and instead aim for an incremental set of market-based reforms that are implemented by the states within broad federal guidelines. In general, the division of responsibility can be delineated clearly. The federal government must reform the mechanisms for subsidizing health insurance so that they remain consistent with cost-conscious consumption and they create a lead role for the states in overseeing the regulation of consumers' insurance options. The federal government must also, however, make adjustments in the federal regulation of insurance to make sure to protect at some basic level all Americans who may develop an expensive health condition.

The key federal and state actions that will advance affordable insurance and high-quality care include the following[13]:

- Convert the federal tax preference for employer-paid premiums into a refundable tax credit; this initiative should start with workers in small firms and individuals who are not in stable medium or large employer-based plans today;

- Establish a federal-state partnership to protect those with pre-existing conditions, which takes the form of state administered high-risk pools financed by the federal government; and
- Reform the significant portion of the Medicaid program covering the non-elderly poor, allowing states to integrate these program participants into the same insurance arrangements which cover other working age Americans.

State Implementation of Federally-Financed Tax Credits for Coverage

In 2008, while running for president, Senator John McCain proposed to end the tax break for employer-paid health insurance premiums and replace it with a refundable tax credit for all insurance purchasers, whether they buy insurance through their employers or on the individual market.

There is little doubt that the McCain plan would have addressed many of the shortcomings prevalent in health care today. Under this plan, workers could acquire portable insurance, eliminating job lock (the tendency of people to stick with jobs they do not like just for the insurance), and closing gaps in coverage for those temporarily out of the workforce. Millions of workers who are now passive enrollees in their company plans would become cost-conscious consumers looking for value in the marketplace. With a fixed tax credit that does not change based on the insurance purchased, workers would have strong financial incentives to sign up for low-premium offerings, and insurers would have incentives to meet the market demand with lower cost insurance plans and greater efficiency.

Further, the universal tax credit would create incentives that will quickly lead to near-universal coverage. Every household would receive the tax credit — even ones that pay no income taxes. All experience indicates most households will buy something so as not to let the credit go to waste. Such a policy prescription would cause a dramatic reduction in the ranks of the uninsured.

Unfortunately, then-Senator Barack Obama relentlessly denounced the McCain plan during the 2008 campaign with distorted attacks and badly damaged the idea in the public's mind. Moreover, the McCain plan's extensive reach may be too much for the country to take on all at once. Most Americans believe we need reform especially to provide better coverage for their fellow citizens. At the same time tens of millions of Americans are also generally satisfied with the insurance plans that their large employers provide for them today, and are very reluctant to have that disrupted.

A new effort to move toward a defined contribution tax subsidy for working age Americans must therefore separate the marketplace into two groups.

First, it will allow the well-insured (those in plans run by medium and larger firms) to remain covered by their current insurance plans. An upper limit on the tax preference for these plans can be established to encourage some additional cost discipline. Individuals working in smaller firms or lacking access to an employer plan will get a new refundable tax credit, similar to the one envisioned in the McCain proposal. This compromise allows a consumer-driven marketplace to become established, while avoiding the political problem of disrupting coverage for those who generally like what they have today.

States will play a critical role in such a reform blueprint. The only federal requirement that should be imposed *on insurers* seeking to offer coverage to credit-eligible Americans is that they provide an upper limit on financial exposure to health expenses for their enrollees. In turn, the states will determine the upper limit of financial exposure.

The states are best suited to serve as the locus of decision-making. States will decide what health benefits, if any, to require in the benefit packages offered by insurers to tax credit-eligible customers. They will decide the manner by which their citizens sign up for insurance plans, and the consumer information that drives enrollments. For instance, they could establish consumer marketplaces, like the Utah Health Exchange, or they could rely on private vendors to facilitate consumer shopping.

There are two federal requirements that should be universal for all states. The first is that states should be required to make it easy for citizens to designate their preferred insurance plan, and that once designated, the state will notify the U.S. Treasury to ensure payment of the credit to the appropriate plan. Second, states should establish systems for assigning tax credit-eligible citizens to default plans should some citizens fail to make a choice on their own.

The key to making this work is cost-conscious consumer choice. With a fixed tax credit, when residents choose high premium plans, they must pay the extra premiums out of their own pockets. When they choose less expensive plans, they will get to use dollars saved for other health care expenses. Tax credit payments not used to pay insurance premiums will be deposited into individually-owned health savings accounts to be used to pay out-of-pocket health expenses on a tax-free basis.

Although many millions of Americans will remain outside of state insurance regulation due to the retention of ERISA and large employer-based coverage, the number will be limited and will likely decline slowly in ensuing years. As a result, a growing number of Americans will receive their insurance through state-regulated plans, which will give states enhanced leverage to oversee both insurance rules and the medical delivery system.

To ensure that this large influx of new state-regulated insurance enrollees is treated fairly, the federal government should also require states to establish a behind-the-scenes risk-adjustment system among private insurers offering plans in the new marketplace. Such a mechanism will require participating insurers to use formulae established in advance to share revenue from premiums with their competitors based on the risk profiles of those selecting their plans. Insurers serving more unhealthy enrollees than average will thus get compensation from insurers covering healthier-than-average groups. This will help states maintain a robust insurance marketplace where competition centers on delivering value for patients and insurance enrollees, not on avoidance of those needing more extensive medical care.

Covering Pre-Existing Conditions with State-Based High Risk Pools

A new system of refundable tax credits will go a long way toward broadening insurance coverage and reducing the ranks of the uninsured. But an additional step is needed to ensure those who develop an expensive health condition are not penalized in a market-based insurance system: extend to all Americans who remain in continuous coverage protection against being assessed excessively high premiums based on risk profiles. As Tom Miller explains in his chapter *The Case for Competition, Choice, and a Healthy Federalism,* this objective can be achieved through a coordinated federal-state high risk pool initiative.

The changes necessary to make effective high-risk pools a reality are reasonably straightforward. Workers who leave job-based plans for the individual market should be able to do so without being required, as they are today, to stay in their former employer's plan for eighteen months. As Miller notes, many workers do not even realize that they must satisfy this requirement in order to retain their pre-existing condition protections. Instead of such a convoluted process, workers should be able to move directly from an employer-provided plan to an individual policy financed by a refundable tax credit without being denied coverage or assessed large premiums in cases where they develop an expensive health condition while insured.

Next, within a federal framework, there should be state-imposed limits on underwriting health insurance for people moving from the employer-based market to the individual market. The most effective approach would be to cap premiums for high-risk insurance enrollees who have maintained continuous insurance coverage at no more than a fixed percentage of standard rates (perhaps 150 percent).

Limiting premiums for these individuals means that they will be paying premiums that fall well short of what they would be charged with full underwriting. The difference will need to be bridged with transparent and explicit taxpayer subsidies, which in a reformed system can be achieved by adequately funding existing state high-risk pools. The annual federal cost of socializing the premiums for these high-risk individuals is likely somewhere between $10 billion and $20 billion annually.

Congress will have to provide these funds, and should do so in the form of a capped annual appropriation to the states. Congress should also give states wide latitude to determine how eligibility will be ascertained and compensated.

For their part, states will need to structure the risk pools in a way that prevents private insurers from attempting to move insurance enrollees who are not truly high-risk out of their risk pool and into the publicly subsidized high-risk pools. States can accomplish that by giving independent health risk assessors the authority to penalize insurers for sending referrals to the high-risk pool of individuals who are determined not to be truly high-risk.

Once a worker has entered the individual insurance market, they should not have to face repeated health risk assessments, as can happen today when they switch insurance carriers. Instead, this new federal-state framework should stipulate that new entrants into the individual market would be required to get a risk evaluation only once; once approved for coverage in that market, they would have the right to renew their policies with any licensed insurer in the state based on their initial risk evaluation.

Also, to encourage as much enrollment in health insurance as possible, there should be a one-time open enrollment option for the uninsured to sign up for coverage and secure protection under the new pre-existing condition rules.

The approach to covering pre-existing conditions described above will not be inexpensive. But the cost of state high-risk pools will be a fraction of the cost of the PPACA, and the state pools lack the mandates and onerous rules contained in the PPACA. To address the issue of pre-existing conditions, transparent subsidies are preferable to the PPACA's innumerable insurance regulations.

Letting States Implement Market-Based Medicaid Reforms

The Medicaid program serves three distinct populations. First, there are the so-called dually eligible beneficiaries: individuals eligible both for Medicare and Medicaid. In the main, these are poor senior citizens who need extensive long-term care, often including nursing home stays. Second, there are the long-term disabled who are not elderly but who need support over a long period of time. Third, there are individuals and families enrolled in Medicaid for coverage of their primary and acute health care needs. In general, Medicaid was originally created to cover this last group of low-income individuals and families as part of a system of welfare support. Typically, Medicaid participants in this last group are mothers with dependent children who receive cash welfare support from the state.

Those who would reform Medicaid need to formulate different strategies to deal with the different challenges of these distinct populations. The reform proposal presented here deals only with the third group of Medicaid users, those who are not elderly and not disabled, or roughly 75 percent of Medicaid enrollees.

Originally, states established automatic "categorical" Medicaid eligibility when they signed up an individual or family for cash welfare support; primarily, this occurred under the Aid to Families with Dependent Children (AFDC) program. In recent years, however, states have moved away from that approach. Eligibility for coverage is now more often based strictly on income tests. Yet even today, Medicaid is not integrated into or coordinated with the insurance system for working-age Americans. This lack of coordination between the two insurance systems creates serious problems for Medicaid beneficiaries: when poor individuals and families get better paying jobs, they often lose eligibility for Medicaid support. These individuals lose Medicaid eligibility even when they are faced with uncertain insurance prospects in the employer market. In effect, these arrangements act as a strong disincentive to secure better employment and move up the wage scale. Movement back and forth between Medicaid and private insurance plans can also disrupt ongoing relationships with physicians who are in private insurance networks, but not part of a state's Medicaid plan.

A move to replace both traditional Medicaid assistance and the tax preference for employer-paid health insurance with a refundable tax credit will open up new possibilities for explicit and beneficial coordination between the Medicaid program and the types of coverage normally available to working-age Americans. For example, using their authority to regulate benefits, levels of premium assistance, and other features of the insurance market, states can explicitly design the refundable tax credit so that it serves those who are eligible for Medicaid (though not the disabled or dually eligible). Such an approach will allow policymakers to restructure Medicaid so that it serves as supplemental premium support for the poor. In order to avoid creating large disincentives for the beneficiaries to climb the wage and income ladder on their own, states can, over time, phase down the add-on Medicaid payments.

The federal portion of the restructured Medicaid program can, in fact, be converted into a per capita allotment system which is based on current federal spending for a state's Medicaid program. This would enable a movement away from today's system of federal matching payments to states and toward a system of fixed federal payments. The per capita allotment system will free states to manage funding in ways that are appropriate to each state, and remove the incentives that push federal matching payments upward every year.

Putting Medicaid enrollees into the same federal tax credit system as other working age Americans would facilitate portable insurance for low-income families who are struggling to move up the wage ladder. For instance, if states allowed their Medicaid-eligible citizens to use the federal tax credit to enroll in the same plans available to workers who also get the tax credit, then the Medicaid enrollees could keep their insurance plans even when they get better paying jobs.

Medicaid reform of this kind is a form of defined contribution health care. The Medicaid participants would get a large share of their premiums subsidized by the federal tax credit plus additional Medicaid support. But they would still face additional costs if they were to choose more expensive coverage options. This should encourage even the Medicaid population to seek higher value health care options.

In this reform, states would be given great flexibility to alter the mix of benefits, beneficiary cost-sharing, and the extent of managed care requirements much more so than what is currently allowable under Medicaid.

Since its enactment in the 1960s, Medicaid has mainly been considered a health insurance program for non-working welfare recipients and others who cannot access employer-sponsored coverage. Moving from a defined benefit to defined contribution structure, and freeing states to implement this program in a way that is consistent with other insurance regulation will dramatically reform the existing Medicaid program, a program which by the day proves less and less financially tenable. Utilizing a system of defined contributions, Medicaid could be integrated into the same private insurance marketplace populated with workers and their families, allowing more seamless transitions as Medicaid recipients move into higher paying jobs.

Conclusion

The most serious medium- and long-term economic challenge our nation faces is that the federal government has committed itself to spending far more than it can collect in taxes. The government has made promises it cannot keep. The primary reason for this growing gap between liabilities and resources is the rapidly rising cost of federal health programs. The combined cost of Medicare and Medicaid is already 5.5 percent of GDP, and these costs are expected to double with the retirement of the baby boom generation.

One-off ideas for trimming individual federal reimbursements for medical care will not solve this problem. What is needed is a continuous, long-term, dynamic process that will lead those who deliver services in the health sector to provide better care at lower cost. What can bring that about?

PPACA is filled with provisions that are aimed at giving the federal government the power to re-engineer how American health care is delivered. Proponents of this point of view believe that the federal government has the know-how and the capacity to tweak reimbursement policies in ways that can prompt hospitals, doctors, and other providers to become more efficient.

There is no substantial evidence for this point of view. Indeed, instead of improving the efficiency of the health sector, budget cuts imposed by the federal government have tended to make matters worse with blunt, across-the-board cost-cutting. Politicians find it unpalatable to pick winners and losers among hospitals and physician groups by calling out providers that offer sub-standard care. As a result, to cut spending, they vote for across-the-board payment reductions. Over time, using payment reductions to cut costs has the predictable result of driving willing suppliers of services out of the marketplace. For this reason, many Medicaid patients have a difficult time finding a doctor who will care for them.

The alternative to the failed top-down approach of government micromanagement is a decentralized approach that allows individuals and states to find solutions that work for them. The most important feature of such a system is price-conscious consumers selecting among competing insurers and delivery systems based on price and quality.

With cost-conscious consumers looking for the best value for their money, cost-cutting innovations are rewarded, not punished as they are today. Physicians and hospitals have strong financial incentives to reorganize themselves to increase productivity and efficiency in order to capture a larger share of a highly competitive marketplace.

Building such a marketplace will require a number of changes at both the federal and state levels of government. Building a functioning marketplace will not work unless the states and federal government are working in concert to achieve it. The federal government must reform the way it subsidizes health insurance for workers and those on Medicaid, and it must close cracks in today's system of insurance protections for those with pre-existing conditions. States must then adjust the way they regulate insurance and run Medicaid in order to facilitate cost-conscious consumer choice and ease of administration for their citizens.

This policy prescription is complex, but the payoff will be immense. With a robust federal-state partnership, Americans will get a more affordable and more patient-focused health system. Indeed, they will get the kind of health system they have always wanted, a system characterized by high-quality care, predictable expenses, and the ability of customers to make informed choices that best suit their needs.

Endnotes

Introduction

1. Jeffrey Flier, "Health 'Reform' Gets a Failing Grade," *Wall Street Journal*, November 17, 2009.

Chapter 1

1. Under the Employee Retirement Income Security Act (ERISA) of 1974, employer-sponsored pension and welfare benefit plans, including group health insurance plans, are exempt from some or all state regulation. Self-insured plans in which plan sponsors themselves pay claims are entirely exempt from state regulation, but fully insured plans in which the employer purchases coverage from a commercial insurer are subject to some laws indirectly through state regulation of their commercial insurers. If an employee suffers serious health problems because of denial of coverage under an employer-sponsored health plan, the employee must seek redress in federal court. ERISA limits money damages from self-insured and insured plans to the cost of an improperly denied service. ERISA exempts all employer sponsored health plans from punitive or compensatory damages in civil suits, brought under state law, that charge improper denial or processing of an employee's health coverage. Although courts have carved out more exceptions to broad ERISA protection from state-based legal claims over the last decade or two, ERISA still generally protects insurers and other third parties from tort liability and other state claims when they are performing services on behalf of an employer health plan. Similarly, although several newer federal laws have imposed additional mandates on self-insured employer health plans, ERISA still prevents states from applying consumer protection laws, mandated benefit requirements, premium taxes, and other state-based insurance requirements to self-insured employer health plans. Employers and health plans contend that ERISA protections afford them the flexibility they need to hold down health care costs and provide essential benefits. ERISA protec-

tions also allow self-insured multistate employers to adopt uniform benefits packages instead of fine-tuning them to deal with a patchwork of state laws and regulations.

2. For example, more extensive "small group" portability regulations under the 1996 Health Insurance Portability and Accountability Act apply to firms with two to fifty employees, although other ones apply to all employer-sponsored health plans. Continuation insurance coverage rules for former workers under the Consolidated Omnibus Budget Reconciliation Act of 1985 apply to firms with 20 or more employees. See Brigitte C. Madrian, "Health Insurance Portability," *Regulation* 21(1).

3. Thomas P. Miller, "How the Tax Exclusion Shaped Today's Private Health Insurance Market," Joint Economic Committee, December 17, 2003, available at http://www.aei.org/docLib/20070222_Millerarticle.pdf (accessed September 12, 2011).

4. Congressional Research Service, "PPACA Provisions and Potential use of Executive Orders," Memorandum to Senator Tom Coburn, November 14, 2011.

Chapter 2

1. For a previous analysis of this issue, see James C. Capretta and Tom Miller, "How to Cover Pre-existing Conditions," *National Affairs* 2010 (4): 110-126.

2. By one recent measure, the number of people covered by employment-based health insurance in 2010 was about 169 million (roughly 55 percent of the total population). Carmen DeNavas-Walt, Bernadette D. Proctor, and Jessica C. Smith, "Income, Poverty, and Health Insurance Coverage in the United States: 2010," United States Census Bureau Current Population Reports P60-239, pp. 23, 29, 77, available at www.census.gov/pro/2011pubs/p60-239. pdf (accessed October 15, 2011). See also Paul Fronstin, "Sources of Health Insurance and Characteristics of the Uninsured: Analysis of the March 2011 Current Population Survey," Employee Benefit Research Institute Issue Brief No. 362, September 2011, p. 5 (providing a lower estimate of 156 million people, or 57.5 percent of the nonelderly population), available at http:/ssrn. com/abstract=1933845 (accessed October 17, 2011).

3. Craig Copeland, "Employee Tenure: Stable Overall, But Male and Female Trends Differ," *Employee Benefit Research Institute Notes* 26(3).

4. Anthony T. Lo Sasso, "An Examination of State Non-Group and Small-Group Health Insurance Regulations," AEI Online, January 3, 2008, available at http://www.aei.org/docLib/20080111_LoSassoState.pdf (accessed September 14, 2011).

5. In recent years, COBRA premiums were more heavily subsidized by taxpayers for a relatively short period of time in the aftermath of the deep recession

of 2007-2009.

6. Bradley Herring, Xue Song, and Mark Pauly, "Changes in Coverage in the Individual and Group Health Insurance Markets and the Effect of Health Status," Prepared for Office of Disability, Aging and Long-Term Care Policy, Office of the Assistant Secretary for Planning and Evaluation, U. S. Department of Health and Human Services Contract #HHS-100-03-0022, April 2008, available at http://aspe.hhs.gov/daltcp/reports/2008/HIcover.pdf (accessed October 13, 2011).

7. Scott E. Harrington and Gregory R. Niehaus, *Risk Management and Insurance.* (New York: Irwin/McGraw-Hill 1999).

8. See, for example, United States Government Accountability Office, "Health Insurance: Enrollment, Benefits, Funding, and Other Characteristics of State High-Risk Health Insurance Pools," GAO-09-730R, July 22, 2009, available at http://www.gao.gov/new.items/d09730r.pdf (accessed October 5, 2011) and James C. Capretta and Thomas P. Miller, "How to Cover Pre-existing Conditions," *National Affairs* 2010 (4): 115.

9. Mark V. Pauly and Bradley Herring, *Pooling Health Insurance Risks* (Washington: AEI Press 1999).

10. Mark V. Pauly and Bradley Herring, "Risk Pooling and Regulation: Policy and Reality in Today's Individual Health Insurance Market," *Health Affairs* 26(3): 770-779; LoSasso, 2008.

11. A few other states struggled to maintain the toxic combination of community rating and guaranteed issue in their individual insurance markets, with little success and various side effects. See ibid.

12. See John F. Cogan, R. Glenn Hubbard, and Daniel P. Kessler, "The Effect of Medicare Coverage for the Disabled on the Market for Private Insurance," National Bureau of Economic Research working paper no. 14309, September 2008.

13. United States Government Accountability Office, 2009.

14. See Thomas P. Miller, "Fixing Private Health Insurance: Protection against Health Risk Redefinition," presentation at American Enterprise Institute conference -- Private Health Insurance Markets: Facts, Fables, and Fixes, October 21, 2009, slides 6 and 7 summarizing 2001 Medical Expenditure Panel Survey findings, available at http://www.aei.org/docLib/Miller%20Fixing%20Private%20Health%20Insurance.pdf (accessed October 6, 2011).

15. United States Government Accountability Office, 2009.

16. Mark V. Pauly, *Health Reform without Side Effects: Making Markets Work for Individual Health Insurance.* (Stanford: Hoover Press 2010), http://media.hoover.org/sites/default/files/documents/9780817910440_1.pdf (accessed September 18, 2011).

17. United States Government Accountability Office, 2009.

18. Ibid.

19. See, for example, Karen Pollitz, "State High-Risk Health Insurance Pools," NIHCM Foundation, April 2009, available at http://www.nihcm.org/pdf/ExpertVoices_Pollitz_FINAL.pdf (accessed October 7, 2011); Linda J. Blumberg and Timothy A. Waidmann, "Increasing Health Insurance Coverage for High-Cost Older Adults," AARP Public Policy Institute research report, July 2009, available at http://www.urban.org/uploadedpdf/1001296_increasing-healthinsurance.pdf (accessed October 7, 2011); Linda J. Blumberg, Lisa Clemens-Cope, and Fredric Blavin, "Lowering Financial Burdens and Increasing Health Insurance Coverage for Those with High Medical Costs," Urban Institute Health Policy Briefs no. 17, December 2005, available at http://www.urban.org/UploadedPDF/311261_financial_burdens.pdf (accessed October 8, 2011).

20. See, for example, Kevin Sack, "McCain Plan to Aid States on Health Could Be Costly," *New York Times*, July 9, 2011, available at http://www.nytimes.com/2008/07/09/us/politics/09health.html?pagewanted=all (accessed November 7, 2011).

21. Those requirements are not fully phased in until January 2014, when additional coverage options through an expansion of Medicaid and new state-based health benefits exchanges are supposed to be implemented.

22. Richard S. Foster, Office of the Actuary, Centers for Medicare and Medicaid Services, "Estimated Financial Effects of the 'Patient Protection and Affordable Care Act', as Amended," April 22, 2010, available at https://www.cms.gov/ActuarialStudies/downloads/PPACA_2010-04-22.pdf (accessed October 18, 2011).

23. United States Government Accountability Office, "Pre-Existing Condition Insurance Plans: Program Features, Early Enrollment and Spending Trends, and Federal Oversight Activities," GAO-11-662, July 2011, available at http://www.gao.gov/new.items/d11662.pdf (accessed October 10, 2011); U.S Department of Health & Human Services, "State by State Enrollment in the Pre-Existing Condition Insurance Plan, as of August 31, 2011," available at http://www.healthcare.gov/news/factsheets/2011/10/pcip10142011a.html (accessed November 7, 2011).

24. See, for example, U.S. Department of Health and Human Services, "Coverage Denied: How the Current Health Insurance System Leaves Millions Behind," (suggesting that up to 12.6 million Americans recently had been discriminated against by insurers on the basis of their health status), available at http://www.healthreform.gov/reports/denied_coverage/coveragedenied.pdf (accessed October 13, 2011); and U.S. Department of Health and Human Services, "At Risk: Pre-Existing Conditions Could Affect 1 in 2 Americans: 129 Million People Could Be Denied Affordable Coverage Without Health Reform," (with even more extreme claims blurring the difference between the many people with some existing medical condition and those actually denied

coverage due to their health status), available at http://www.healthcare.gov/ law/resources/reports/preexisting.html (accessed October 15, 2011).
25. United States Government Accountability Office, 2011.

Chapter 3

1. See, for example, Frank A. Sloan, Christopher J. Conover, and Mark A. Hall, "State Strategies to Reduce the Growing Numbers of People without Health Insurance." *Regulation* 22(3): 24–31; Gail A. Jensen and Michael A. Morrisey, "Employer-Sponsored Health Insurance and Mandated Benefit Laws." *Milbank Quarterly* 77(4): 425–59; Amanda E. Kowalski , William J. Congdon, and Mark H. Showalter, "State Health Insurance Regulations and the Price of High-Deductible Policies," *Forum for Health Economics & Policy* 11(2), available at http://www.bepress.com/fhep/11/2/8 (accessed September 10, 2011); James W. Henderson, Tracey LaPierre, Christopher J. Conover, J. Allen Seward, and Beck A. Taylor, "Estimating the Impact of State Health Insurance Mandates on Premium Costs in the Individual Market Using the Community Tracking Survey," *Journal of Insurance Regulation* 23(3): 3-36; Melinda L. Shriver and Grace-Marie Arnett, "Uninsured Rates Rise Dramatically in States with Strictest Health Insurance Regulations," Heritage Foundation Backgrounder No. 1211, August 14, 1998, Washington, D.C.
2. See Roberta Romano, "Law as a Product: Some Pieces of the Incorporation Puzzle," *Journal of Law, Economics, & Organization* 1(2): 225–83; Jonathan R. Macey, "Federal Deference to Local Regulators and the Economic Theory of Regulation: Toward a Public-Choice Explanation of Federalism," *Virginia Law Review* 76 (March 1990): 265–91.
3. Tiebout pioneered an economic theory of federalism that argued that competition among local jurisdictions allows citizens to match their preferences with particular menus of local public goods: Charles M. Tiebout, "A Pure Theory of Local Expenditures," *Journal of Political Economy* 64(5): 416–24, Qian and Weingast noted that inter-jurisdiction competition, along with decentralization of information and authority, can provide credible commitment to secure economic rights and preserve markets: Yingyi Qian and Barry R. Weingast, "Federalism as a Commitment to Preserving Market Incentives," *Journal of Economic Perspectives* 11(4): 83–92.
4. See, for example, Representative John Shadegg, Health Choice Act of 2007, H.R. 4460, available at http://thomas.loc.gov/cgi-bin/bdquery/D?d110:7:./ temp/~bdex77 (accessed September 16, 2011).
5. Tarren Bragdon and Joel Allumbaugh, "Health Care Reform in Maine: Reversing 'Obamacare Lite,'" Heritage Foundation Backgrounder no. 2582, July 18, 2011, Washington, D.C.

6. Ted Cruz and Mario Loyola. "Shield of Federalism: Interstate Compacts in Our Constitution," Texas Public Policy Foundation, December 2010, Austin, TX.

7. Ibid.

8. For more details, see Healthcarecompact.org, "The Compact," available at http://healthcarecompact.org/compact (accessed November 9, 2011).

9. Stephen T. Parente, Roger Feldman, Jean Abraham, and Yi Xu, "Consumer Response to a National Marketplace for Individual Health Insurance," *The Journal of Risk and Insurance* (2010): 1-23.

10. Aparna Mathur, "Comments on Consumer Response to a National Marketplace for Individual Insurance," American Enterprise Institute, July 31, 2008, available at http://www.aei.org/docLib/20080731_MathurPresentation.pdf (accessed September 14, 2011).

11. Over 30 states require some type of public reporting of hospital charges or reimbursement rates. Some states' all-payer, all-claims database extends in part to reporting of emergency room and/or ambulatory procedure charges. For example, the state of Minnesota's web portal lists the average payment made by health insurance plans for over 100 common medical procedures, including lab services, office visits, mental health care, and obstetrical services. South Dakota's hospital pricing website in 2008 expanded its listing of median prices for the top 25 inpatient procedures at hospitals in the state to other outpatient procedures. Wisconsin was among the first set of states to require individual hospitals to submit data on their prices and lengths of stay, but the information did not begin to reach the general public effectively until the state delegated that task to the Wisconsin Hospital Association in 2003. National Conference of State Legislatures, "State Legislation Relating to Transparency and Disclosure of Health and Hospital Charges," September 2011, available at http://www.ncsl.org/default.aspx?tabid=14512 (accessed October 17, 2011).

12. Ha T. Tu and Johanna Lauer, "Impact of Health Care Price Transparency on Price Variation: The New Hampshire Experience," Center for Studying Health System Change issue brief no. 128, November 2009, available at http://hschange.org/CONTENT/1095 (accessed October 18, 2011).

13. Thomas P. Miller, Troyen A. Brennan, and Arnold Milstein, "How Can We Make More Progress in Measuring Physicians' Performance to Improve the Value of Care," *Health Affairs* 28(5): 1429-1437.

Chapter 4

1. James C. Capretta and Thomas P. Miller, "A Defined Contribution Route to Health Care Choice and Competition," AEI Online, December 7, 2010, avail-

able at http://www.aei.org/docLib/Defined-Contribution-Route-to-Health-Care-Choice.pdf (accessed October 7, 2011).

2. Cynthia Shirk, "Premium Assistance: An Update," National Health Policy Forum Background Paper no. 80, October 12, 2010; and U.S. Government Accountability Office, "Medicaid and CHIP: Enrollment, Benefits, Expenditures, and other Characteristics of State Premium Assistance Programs," GAO-10-258R, January 19, 2010.

3. Will Fox and John Pickering, "Hospital and Physician Cost Shift: Payment Level Comparison of Medicare, Medicaid, and Commercial Payers," Milliman, December 2008, available at http://publications.milliman.com/research/health-rr/pdfs/hospital-physician-cost-shift-RR12-01-08.pdf (accessed August 31, 2011). Federal approval of state premium-assistance plan waivers also requires states to demonstrate their cost-effectiveness compared to traditional state Medicaid coverage and guarantee that they will offer comparable health benefits and protection against cost sharing.

4. Richard Teske, "Abolishing the Medicaid Ghetto: Putting 'Patients First,'" (Washington, DC: American Legislative Exchange Council, 2002), available at http://infoassist.panpha.org/docushare/dsweb/Get/Document-11708/abolishing%20the%20medicaid%20ghette.pdf (accessed November 23, 2010).

5. See, for example, Michael Bond, "Reforming Medicaid in Florida," James Madison Institute, Backgrounder Number 65, April 2010, available at www.jamesmadison.org/wp-content/uploads/pdf/materials/Bkgrnder_Reform-Medicaid_BondApril10.pdf (accessed November 23, 2010); Joan Alker, Jack Hoadley, and Jennifer Thompson, "Florida's Experience with Medicaid Reform: What Has Been Learned in the First Two Years," (Washington, DC: Georgetown University, Health Policy Institute, October 2008), available at http://hpi.georgetown.edu/floridamedicaid/pdfs/briefing7.pdf (accessed November 23, 2010); and Agency for Health Care Administration, "Florida Medicaid: Year 4 Draft Annual Report (2010)," available at http://ahca.myflorida.com/medicaid/medicaid_reform/pdf/reform_draft_annual_report_yr4_070109-063010.pdf (accessed November 24, 2010).

6. Mark V. Pauly and Thomas W. Granneman, *Medicaid Everyone Can Count On: Public Choices for Equity and Efficiency* (Washington, DC: AEI Press, 2010); and Robert B. Helms, "The SCHIP Open: Hidden Incentives for States to Spend Federal Funds," AEI *Health Policy Outlook*, August 2007, available at www.aei.org/outlook/26708 (accessed November 24, 2010).

7. The following section is adapted in large part from the forthcoming American Enterprise Institute study by John Stephen, "Taking Medicaid off Federally Funded Steroids: Putting It Back on a Nutritious Diet of State-Centered Reform."

8. Section 1902(a)(10)(B) of the Social Security Act. See also U.S. Social Security Administration, "Medicaid Program Description and Legislative History,"

Annual Statistical Supplement, 2010, available at http://www.ssa.gov/policy/docs/statcomps/supplement/2010/medicaid.html (accessed October 1, 2011).

9. For a further description of current federal government restrictions on states' use of alternative payment methodologies, insurance plan control over provider networks, cost sharing, and number of managed care plans offered to beneficiaries, see Republican Governors Public Policy Committee Health Care Task Force, "A New Medicaid: A Flexible, Innovative and Accountable Future," August 30, 2011, p. 10. available at http://online.wsj.com/public/resources/documents/RGAMedicaidReport.pdf (accessed October 7, 2011).

10. See *White v. Beal*, 555 F.2d 1146, 1151-52 (3d Cir.1977); *Parry By and Through Parry v. Crawford*, 990 F.Supp. 1250, 1257 (D.Nev.1998). See generally *Sobk y v. Smoley*, 855 F.Supp. 1123, 1140-41 (E.D.Cal.1994) (citing cases).

11. 42 U.S.C. § 1396a(a)(23).

12. Senate Finance Committee and Senate House Energy and Commerce Committee, "Medicaid Expansion in the New Law: Cost to the States," Joint Report, March 1, 2011, available at http://thehill.com/images/stories/blogs/medicaidcost.pdf (accessed June 15, 2011).

13. U.S. Department of Health and Human Services, "2008 Actuarial Report on the Financial Outlook for Medicaid," available at https://www.cms.gov/ActuarialStudies/downloads/MedicaidReport2008.pdf (accessed October 10, 2011).

14. Under the Global Waiver, the State of Rhode Island was not given a predetermined allotment of funds to use in the program. It still had to administer Medicaid funds within the federal matching rate requirements, which means that the state has to have expenditure from its own state general fund revenue that is then matched by the federal funds at the state match rate, and the program is administered under this funding relationship.

15. Florida Agency for Health Care Administration, "Florida Medicaid Reform, Year 4 Annual Draft Report," p. 99 available at http://www.fdhc.state.fl.us/medicaid/medicaid_reform/pdf/reform_draft_annual_report_yr4_070109-063010.pdf (accessed June 10, 2011).

16. Ibid, table 46.

17. Ibid, page 61.

18. Paul Duncan, "Evaluating Medicaid Reform in Florida: Lessons for Other States," Presentation for the National Medicaid Congress, June 8, 2010, available at http://mre.phhp.ufl.edu/talkspresentations/The%20National%20Medicaid%20Congress_Paul%20Duncan_Final%20PPT_06-08-2010.pdf, slide 17 (accessed June 14, 2011).

19. Several other more limited examples include Oklahoma's SoonerCare use of utilization review to identify and educate frequent Medicaid emergency room (ER) users, which led to a 48 percent reduction in ER visits and savings of more than $12 million from January 2006 to March 2009. Pennsylvania's

Healthy Hoops program targeted the population at risk for asthma, leading to a 10 percent increase in medication adherence and a dramatic decline in asthma-related ER use. Republican Governors Public Policy Committee Health Care Task Force, "A New Medicaid: A Flexible, Innovative and Accountable Future," page 6.

20. Katherine Gifford, Vernon K. Smith, Dyke Snipes, and Julia Paradise, "A Profile of Medicaid Managed Care Programs in 2010: Findings from a 50-State Survey," Kaiser Commission on Medicaid and the Uninsured, September 2011, available at http://www.kff.org/medicaid/upload/8220.pdf (accessed October 14, 2011).

21. Mark Duggan and Tamara Hayford, "Has the Shift to Managed Care Reduced Medicaid Expenditures? Evidence from State and Local-Level Mandates," National Bureau of Economic Research working paper no. 17236, available at http://www.nber.org/papers/w17236 (accessed October 13, 2011).

22. Republican Governors Public Policy Committee Health Care Task Force, "A New Medicaid: A Flexible, Innovative and Accountable Future," pages 11, 13.

Chapter 5

1. Division of Health Care Finance and Policy, "Massachusetts Health Care Cost Trends," 2008.

2. John Holahan, Randall R. Bovbjerg, Alison Evans Cuellar, A., Joshua M. Wiener, Susan Flanagan, "Health Policy for Low-Income People in Massachusetts," The Urban Institute, Washington, D.C., 1997.

3. John Holahan, Randall R. Bovbjerg, Jack Hadley, "Caring for the Uninsured in Massachusetts: What Does It Cost, Who Pays and What Would Full Coverage Add to Spending?" Urban Institute for the Blue Cross Blue Shield of Massachusetts Foundation, May 12, 2006.

4. Commonwealth of Massachusetts. Office of the Inspector General, "Ongoing Review of the Uncompensated Care Pool Pursuant to Chapter 240 of the Acts of 2004." Second Report to the House and Senate Committees on Ways and Means. November 2005.

5. W. Mitt Romney, "My Plan for Massachusetts Health Reform," *Boston Globe* 21 November 2004.

6. Scott S. Greenberger, "Business Group Targets Healthcare Tax Proposal says Payroll Levy Bad for Economy," *Boston Globe,* December 23, 2005.

7. Frank Phillips, "Deal Would Charge Firms That Don't Insure Workers," *Boston Globe,* March 4, 2006.

8. The full list of vetoes by Governor Romney included: a provision that extended dental and vision benefits to adult Medicaid beneficiaries and gave beneficiaries who meet certain wellness goals discounts on premiums and co-

payments; a provision that created a larger Public Health Council; a section that allowed "special status aliens," including documented immigrants who have been in the U.S. fewer than five years or those who do not have permanent status, to receive Medicaid benefits regardless of the income of their sponsor; a provision that required a member of the Massachusetts House and Senate to participate in negotiations with the federal government regarding special Medicaid funding; and a provision that prohibited the Romney administration from changing the financing, regulation of or operation of mental health benefits for Medicaid beneficiaries without first submitting its reasoning to the state Legislature.

9. Secretary of Health and Human Services, Commonwealth of Massachusetts, "Chapter 58 Implementation Update," June 12, 2006, accessed at: https://www.mahealthconnector.org/portal/binary/com.epicentric.contentmanagement.servlet.ContentDeliveryServlet/About%2520Us/Publications%2520and%2520Reports/2006/2006-06-12/June12ReportFINAL.pdf (December 12, 2011).
10. Secretary of Health and Human Services, 2006, *[176Q, Section 3]*.
11. W. Mitt Romney, "Health Care for Everyone," *The Wall Street Journal*, April 11, 2006.
12. Massachusetts Health Connector and Department of Revenue, "Data on the Individual Mandate," Tax Year 2008.
13. Division of Health Care Finance and Policy, "Health Care in Massachustts: Key Indicators," 2011.
14. Gorman Actuarial, LLC, "Impact of Merging the Massachusetts Non-Group and Small Group Health Insurance Markets," prepared for the Massachusetts Division of Insurance and Market Merger Special Commission, December 26, 2006.

Chapter 6

1. Chapter 58 of the Acts of 2006, "An Act Providing Access to Affordable, Quality, Accountable Health Care," Chapter 111M, Section 1.
2. Romney's support for a mandate was not seen as an outlier position at the time, as numerous conservative organizations and elected officials supported the concept at a state level, and even some at the national level. Romney never supported the concept of an individual mandate at the national level.
3. The assessment history has been $14.8 million in FY07, $14.4 million in FY08, $16.5 million in FY09, and $17.1 million in FY10. Division of Health Care Finance and Policy, "Fair Share Contribution: Filing Year 2010 Results and Analyses," September 2011, accessed at: http://www.mass.gov/Eeohhs2/docs/dhcfp/r/pubs/11/Fair_Share_Analyses_2010.pdf (November 7, 2011).
4. Chapter 58 of the Acts of 2006, Section 45, part 6.

5. Massachusetts Health Connector, "Affordability Standards Recommended to Connector Board," Press Release, 2007.
6. It should be noted that enrollees may face a premium contribution up to 150% of FPL if they do not choose the lowest cost plan.
7. Chapter 58 of the Acts of 2006, Chapter 176Q, Section 3, Sub-section a, 1.
8. The Connector spent more than $5 million in marketing and outreach efforts in the first year.
9. Massachusetts Executive Office of Health and Human Services, "Chapter 58 Implementation Report Update No. 6," Presented to the Massachusetts State Legislature, April 12, 2007.
10. For more on the design flaws of the Contributory Plan see Joshua D. Archambault, "Massachusetts Health Care Reform Has Left Small Business Behind: A Warning to the States," Heritage Foundation, Backgrounder #2462, Washington, D.C., September 17, 2010.
11. Ibid.
12. Amy Lischko, "Fixing the Massachusetts Health Exchange," The Pioneer Institute, Boston, Massachusetts, March 8, 2011.
13. Most noteworthy is the rejection of premium increase by the Patrick administration in April of 2010. It should be noted, that according to the Connector, the refusal by certain insurance companies to participate in Commonwealth Choice is going to change in 2012.
14. As the result of a lawsuit, roughly 40,000 legal immigrants will be re-enrolled in the regular Commonwealth Care program shortly.
15. Office of the Inspector General, "Ongoing Analysis of the Health Safety Net Trust Fund and Other Health Care Issues," Commonwealth of Massachusetts, accessed at: http://www.mass.gov/ig/publ/hlth_2011_rpt.pdf (October 26, 2011).
16. Massachusetts Division of Health Care and Finance Policy, "Health Safety Net: 2010 Annual Report," December, 2010.
17. Commonwealth of Massachusetts Health Care Quality and Cost Council, My Health Care Options, accessed at: http://hcqcc.hcf.state.ma.us/Content/AboutUs.aspx (October 26, 2011).
18. Chapter 288 of the Acts of 2010, "An Act to Promote Cost Containment, Transparency and Efficiency in the Provision of Quality Health Insurance for Individuals and Small Businesses," signed August 10, 2010, accessed at: http://www.malegislature.gov/Laws/SessionLaws/Acts/2010/Chapter288 (November 7, 2011).
19. Amy Lischko and Kristin Manzolillo, "An Interim Report Card on Massachusetts Health Care Reform, Part 4: Cost-Effective Quality," (April, 2010) Accessed at: http://pioneerinstitute.org/pdf/100429_interim_report_card4.pdf (November 7, 2011).
20. Massachusetts Medicaid Policy Institute, "MassHealth Enrollment Growth

Since Reform," May 17, 2011, accessed at: http://www.massmedicaid.org/~/media/MMPI/Files/MassHealth%20Enrollment%20Growth%20Chart.pdf, (December 10, 2011).

Chapter 7

1.   Michael Miltenberger and Steve Poftak, "Massachusetts Healthcare Reform: A Framework for Evaluation," Policy Brief, Shamie Center for Better Government, Pioneer Institute, January 2009.

2.   Amy Lischko and Anand Gopalsami, "An Interim Report Card on Massachusetts Health Care Reform. Part 1: Increasing Access," Pioneer Institute, No 49, January 2010.
     Amy Lischko and Kristin Manzolillo, "An Interim Report Card on Massachusetts Health Care Reform. Part 2: Equitable and Sustainable Financing." Pioneer Institute, No. 51, February 2010.
     Amy Lischko and Kristin Manzolillo, "An Interim Report Card on Massachusetts Health Care Reform. Part 3: Administrative Efficiency," Pioneer Institute, No. 55, March 2010.
     Amy Lischko and Kristin Manzolillo, "An Interim Report Card on Massachusetts Health Care Reform. Part 4: Cost-Effective Quality," Pioneer Institute, No. 59, April 2010.

3.   Derek Delia and Joel Cantor, "Emergency Department Utilization and Capacity," Robert Wood Johnson Foundation, The Synthesis Project, July 2009.

4.   Division of Health Care Finance and Policy, "Preventable/Avoidable Emergency Department Use in Massachusetts, Fiscal Years 2004 to 2008," July 2010.

5.   Sharon K. Long, Karen Stockley and Heather Dahlen, "Massachusetts Health Reforms: Uninsurance Remains Low, Self-Reported Health Status Improves As State Prepares To Tackle Costs," *Health Affairs*, 10.1377/hlthaff.2011.0653; published ahead of print January 25, 2012.

6.   Centers for Medicare and Medicaid Services, Office of the Actuary, "National Health Statistics Group. Health Expenditure Data, Health Expenditures by State of Residence, 2007," accessed at: http://www.cms.hhs.gov/NationalHealthExpendData/downloads/res-us.pdf. (November 23, 2009.) As cited in Judy Bigby, "Controlling Health Care Costs in Massachusetts after Health Care Reform," *Archives of Internal Medicine*, November 9, 2009; 169 (20): 1833-1835.

7.   Division of Health Care Finance and Policy, "Massachusetts Health Care Cost Trends Historical (1991 – 2004) and Projected (2004 – 2020)," November 2009.

8.   The Commonwealth Fund, "Employer Premiums as Percentage of Median

Household Income Under-65 Population, 2003 and 2009," accessed at: http://www.commonwealthfund.org/usr_doc/site_docs/slideshows/Premium-Trends/PremiumTrends.html (November 10, 2011).

9. U.S. Department of Health & Human Services, Agency for Healthcare Research and Quality, "2006 National Healthcare Quality Report, Ranking on Selected Measures," accessed at: http://statesnapshots.ahrq.gov/snaps06/stat-erankings.jsp?menuId=29&state=MA (October 27, 2011).

Chapter 8

1. Patient Protection and Affordable Care Act of 2010, Public Law 111–148, and Health Care and Education Reconciliation Act of 2010, Public Law 111–152.
2. If a state does not set up a SHOP then small businesses will be able to buy within a AHBE.
3. Public Law 111-148 § Section 1321.
4. Patient Protection and Affordable Care Act of 2010, Public Law 111-148 § Section 1332.
5. Patient Protection and Affordable Care Act of 2010, Public Law 111-148 § Section 1311.
6. Patient Protection and Affordable Care Act of 2010, Public Law 111-148 § Section 1321(c)(1).
7. Patient Protection and Affordable Care Act of 2010, Public Law 111-148 § Section 1311(d)(4). Criteria adapted from Robert Moffit, "Obamacare and Federal Health Exchanges: Undermining State Flexibility," Heritage Foundation, WebMemo #3104, January 18, 2011, accessed at: http://www.heritage.org/Research/Reports/2011/01/Obamacare-and-Federal-Health-Exchanges-Undermining-State-Flexibility#_ftn5 (September 19, 2011).
8. Ibid.
9. From 1980 through 2008, the proportion of private wage and salary workers participating in only defined contribution pension plans increased from 8 percent to 31 percent. Laurence Baker, Kate Bundorf and Anne Royalty, "Consumer Oriented Strategies for Improving Health Benefit Design: An Overview," Technical Review, No. 15, July 2007, Agency for Healthcare Research and Quality, accessed at: http://www.ahrq.gov/downloads/pub/evidence/pdf/consumer/consorient.pdf (September 28, 2011).
10. Jon B. Christianson, Stephen T. Parente and Ruth Taylor, "Defined-Contribution Health Insurance Products: Development And Prospects," *Health Affairs*, 21(1), (2002): 49-64. doi: 10.1377.
11. Ibid.
12. Greg Scandlen, "Defined Contribution Health Insurance," National Center for Policy Analysis Policy Backgrounder No. 154. (2000), Washington, D.C.

13. Patient Protection and Affordable Care Act of 2010, Public Law 111-148 § 1311(d)(4)(F).
14. New § Section 1943(b)(1)(B) of the Social Security Act, as added by Patient Protection and Affordable Care Act of 2010, Public Law 111-148 § 2201.
15. Ed Haislmaier, "A State Lawmaker's Guide to Health Insurance Exchanges," Heritage Foundation Backgrounder #2534, March 21, 2011, accessed at: http://www.heritage.org/Research/Reports/2011/03/A-State-Lawmakers-Guide-to-Health-Insurance-Exchanges (September 28, 2011).
16. Utah Health Exchange, "Exchange Frequently Asked Questions," accessed at: http://www.exchange.utah.gov/learn-more/exchange-frequently-asked-questions (October 5, 2011).
17. Josh Archambault, Pioneer Institute, phone conversation with Norman K. Thurston, PhD, Health Policy & Reform Initiatives Coordinator, Utah Department of Health, September 29, 2011.
18. State of Utah, "H.B. 294 Enrolled: Health System Reform Amendments," 2010 General Session, accessed at: http://le.utah.gov/~2010/bills/hbillenr/hb0294.htm (July 21, 2010).
19. The initial cost was around $650,000, but due to fewer development costs and budget cuts, the budget is currently lower. Josh Archambault, Pioneer Institute, phone conversation with Norman K. Thurston, PhD, Health Policy & Reform Initiatives Coordinator, Utah Department of Health, September 29, 2011.
20. Paul Howard, "Building a Market-Based Health-Insurance Exchange in New York," Medical Progress Report, No 13, April 2011, Manhattan Institute for Policy Research, accessed at: http://www.manhattan-institute.org/html/mpr_13.htm (October 5, 2011).
21. Individuals enrolled in a basic health program are not eligible for subsidized coverage in an exchange. Instead, the state will contract out with insurers or providers for their coverage. The federal government will pay 95 percent of the amount the federal government would have spent if these individuals had been enrolled in an exchange. Federal dollars are placed in a state trust fund. See Patient Protection and Affordable Care Act of 2010. Public Law 111-148 §1331(d)(2).
22. James Stergios and Amy Lischko, "Health Care Fails Small Businesses," *The Boston Globe*, May 12, 2010, accessed at: http://www.boston.com/bostonglobe/editorial_opinion/oped/articles/2010/05/12/health_care_fails_small_businesses (August 16, 2010).
23. Suzanne Curry, "Connector Board Report—November 12th," Health Care for All, November 12, 2009, accessed at: http://blog.hcfama.org/2009/11/12/connector-board-report-%E2%80%93-november-12th (August 4, 2010).
24. Suzanne Curry, "A New Chapter for the Connector: 6/10/10 Board Report," Health Care for All, June 11, 2010, accessed at: http://blog.hcfama.

org/2010/06/11/a-new-chapter-for-the-connector-61010-board-report (August 4, 2010).

25. Board of the Commonwealth Health Insurance Connector Authority, "Minutes," June 10, 2010, accessed at: https://www.mahealthconnector.org/portal/site/connector/menuitem.be34eb79b090a7635734db47e6468a0c (August 17, 2010).

26. The Utah Exchange has roughly 150 plan options, but only 80 or so are presented to the average employee given the geography of where they live and the size of their company. Josh Archambault, Pioneer Institute, phone conversation with Norman K. Thurston, PhD, Health Policy & Reform Initiatives Coordinator, Utah Department of Health, September 29, 2011.

27. Elliot K. Wicks, Mark A. Hall and Jack A. Meyer, "Barriers to Small-Group Purchasing Cooperatives," Economic and Social Research Institute, March 2000, accessed at: http://www.esresearch.org/Documents/HPC.pdf (September 19, 2011).
See also:
Richard E. Curtis, Edward Neuschler and Rafe Forland, "Consumer-Choice Purchasing Pools: Past Tense, Future Perfect?" *Health Affairs* 20(1): 164-168. (2001.)
Elliot K. Wicks, "Health Insurance Purchasing Cooperatives," The Commonwealth Fund, November 2002, accessed at: http://www.cmwf.org/usr_doc/wicks_coops.pdf (September 15, 2011).

Conclusion

1. A self-insured health plan is one in which the employer assumes the financial risk for providing health care benefits to its employees. By contrast, a fully-insured plan is one in which employers pay a fixed premium to an insurance carrier.

2. Congressional Budget Office, "Factors Underlying the Growth in Medicare's Spending for Physicians' Services." Background Paper (2007): Table 4, p. 16.

3. See Congressional Budget Office, "Spending and Enrollment Detail for CBO's March 2011 Baseline: Medicaid," available at http://www.cbo.gov/budget/factsheets/2011b/medicaid.pdf.

4. Joint Committee on Taxation, "Tax Expenditures for Health Care," Publication JCX-66-08, p.5.

5. Congressional Budget Office, "The Budget and Economic Outlook: An Update," August 2011, table 1-1, Washington, D.C., and Congressional Budget Office, "The Budget and Economic Outlook: Fiscal Years 2011 to 2021," January 2011, Table E-1.

6. Washington, D.C. See Table 1-8 of Congressional Budget Office, "The Budget

and Economic Outlook: An Update" for the budgetary effects of extending current tax policy and maintaining current rates for Medicare physician fees.

7. Congressional Budget Office, "The Budget and Economic Outlook: An Update," August 2011, table 1-4, Washington, D.C.

8. Congressional Budget Office, "CBO's Long-Term Budget Outlook," June 2011l. Estimate for 2035 is based on CBO's "extended baseline scenario." See supplemental date for Figure 3-3 at: http://www.cbo.gov/ftpdocs/122xx/doc12212/2011-LTBO-Supplemental-Data.xls.

9. For more on the defined contribution approach to health care reform, see: Congressman Paul Ryan, "The Optimist's Guide to Repeal and Replace," Hoover Institution, September 27, 2011.

10. Conservative opposition to the Part D benefit was primarily against adding a universal prescription drug entitlement to Medicare, not its competitive design structure.

11. Henry J. Kaiser Family Foundation, "The Medicare Prescription Drug Benefit," *Fact Sheet*, October 2010, at http://www.kff.org/medicare/upload/7044-11.pdf (August 17, 2011).

12. Office of the Actuary, Centers for Medicare and Medicaid Services, "Comparison of the Office of the Actuary's original Title I MMA estimates to those underlying the CY 2011 Trustees' Report," 2011, Washington, D.C.

13. Slowing the pace of rising health costs will require a substantial reform of the federal Medicare program, moving it toward a system of cost-conscious consumer choice in a functioning and competitive marketplace. That reform will necessarily be led by the federal government and is outside the scope of the reforms discussed in this chapter. For more on Medicare reform see: James C. Capretta, "The Case for Competition in Medicare," The Heritage Foundation, Backgrounder #2605, September 12, 2011, accessed at: http://www.heritage.org/research/reports/2011/09/the-case-for-competition-in-medicare (December 12, 2011).

Authors

Josh D. Archambault is Pioneer Institute's Director of Health Care Policy and Program Manager for the Middle Cities Initiative. Prior to joining Pioneer, Archambault was selected as a Health Policy Fellow at the Heritage Foundation in Washington, D.C. His research centered on the treatment of small businesses in the implementation of health reform in Massachusetts. He has served as legislative director for State Senator Scott Brown and as senior legislative aide in the Governor's Office of Legislative and Intergovernmental Affairs in the Romney Administration. He holds a master's degree in public policy from Harvard University's Kennedy School and BA degrees in political studies and economics from Gordon College.

James C. Capretta has more than two decades of experience as an analyst of U.S. budget and health care policy, including nearly four years as an Associate Director at the White House Office of Management and Budget (OMB), where he had responsibility for health care, Social Security, education, and welfare programs. Capretta now serves as a Fellow at the Ethics and Public Policy Center, where he provides commentary on health care and fiscal policy matters. His essays and articles appear regularly in prominent national publications and online outlets. He has testified before

Congress and appears frequently as a commentator on television news programs and radio broadcasts. Earlier in his career, Capretta served for a decade in Congress as a senior analyst for health care and entitlement issues. He holds a master's degree in public policy studies from Duke University, and he graduated from the University of Notre Dame in 1985 with a BA in government.

 **Jeffrey S. Flier** is the 21st Dean of the Faculty of Medicine at Harvard University. Flier, an endocrinologist and an authority on the molecular causes of obesity and diabetes, is also the Caroline Shields Walker Professor of Medicine at Harvard Medical School. Previously he had served as Harvard Medical School Faculty Dean for Academic Programs and Chief Academic Officer for Beth Israel Deaconess Medical Center (BIDMC), a Harvard teaching affiliate. Following residency training in internal medicine at Mount Sinai Hospital, Flier moved to the National Institutes of Health as a Clinical Associate. In 1978, he joined the Faculty of Medicine at Harvard Medical School, serving as Chief of the Diabetes Unit at Beth Israel Hospital until 1990, when he was named chief of the hospital's Endocrine Division.

Flier is one of the country's leading investigators in the areas of obesity and diabetes. Flier has authored over 200 scholarly papers and reviews and has held many editorial positions, including Associate Editor of the *Journal of Clinical Investigation*, and has served on the Editorial Boards of *Molecular Endocrinology*, the *Journal of Clinical Endocrinology and Metabolism*, and the *American Journal of Medicine*. He is currently on the Board of Consulting Editors of *Science Magazine*. An elected member of the Institute of Medicine and a fellow of the American Academy of Arts and Sciences, Flier's honors also include the Eli Lilly Award of the American Diabetes Association, the Berson Lecture of the American Physiological Society, and an Honorary Doctorate from the University of Athens. In 2005, he received the Banting Medal from the American Diabetes Association, its highest scientific honor. In 2010, Flier was awarded an Honorary Doctor of Science Degree from the University of Edinburgh and earlier this year he was awarded the 2011 Rolf Luft Award for Metabolic Research by the Karolinska Institute in Stockholm, Sweden. Flier holds a BS from City College of New York, and an MD from Mount Sinai School of Medicine, graduating with the Elster Award for Highest Academic Standing.

Amy M. Lischko is a Pioneer Institute's senior fellow on health care and an associate professor of public health and community medicine at Tufts University School of Medicine. Lischko has over fifteen years of experience working for the Commonwealth of Massachusetts in senior-level management positions, most recently as director of health care policy and commissioner of the Division of Health Care Finance and Policy under Governor Romney. Since leaving state government in 2007, she has provided consulting services to AcademyHealth, Mathematica Policy Research, the National Governor's Association, and individual states including Rhode Island, West Virginia, Minnesota, Maine, the US Virgin Islands, and Washington State. She holds a doctorate degree in health services research from Boston University, a master's in public health and a bachelor's degree in food science and nutrition from the University of Massachusetts at Amherst.

Tom P. Miller is a resident fellow at the American Enterprise Institute, where he focuses on health policy, with particular emphasis on such issues as information transparency, health insurance regulation, and market-based alternatives to the policies of the Patient Protection and Affordable Care Act. He is the co-author of *Why ObamaCare Is Wrong for America* (HarperCollins 2011) and heads AEI's "Beyond Repeal and Replace" project. Miller served as a member of the National Advisory Council for the Agency for Healthcare Research and Quality from 2007 to 2009. He was a senior health policy adviser for the John McCain presidential campaign in 2008. Before joining AEI, Miller served for three years as senior health economist for the Joint Economic Committee of the U.S. Congress. He also has been director of health policy studies at the Cato Institute and director of economic policy studies at the Competitive Enterprise Institute. He is a member of the National Academy of Social Insurance and the State Bar of Georgia. Before coming to Washington, Miller had a real life, as a trial attorney, a journalist, and a sports broadcaster. He holds a bachelor's degree in political science from New York University and a law degree from Duke University.

 Jennifer Heldt Powell is a veteran journalist with more than two decades of experience covering issues that have significantly affected the business and political landscape. As a business reporter for the Boston Herald, she covered the financial challenges of the state's health care industry and the complex impact on consumers, insurers and providers. She wrote about the health care reform debate as it grew from vague ideas and general notions to specific plans and finally into law. She currently writes Small Business Matters, a weekly column for the Boston Herald that addresses the concerns of entrepreneurs and small business owners. The column provides a behind-the-scenes look at individual companies and insights into the issues facing small businesses including the economic landscape, health care and policy changes. Powell founded the Excellent Writers Group in 2006 to provide strategic communication consultation to businesses and non-profits. She is a graduate of the University of Wisconsin with degrees in political science and psychology.